The sneaker is a staple of the modern world. The young and old have closets full of them. What does it take to make a sneaker?

It takes an army of people. People to design, develop, manufacture and deliver the sneakers to you. From the hard work of designers, developers, product managers, production teams, pattern masters, stitchers and rubber pressers, here is how it all comes together.

Available now:
*How to Start Your Own Shoe Company*
*How Shoes are Made*
*Shoe Material Design Guide*

Coming Fall 2018:
*How to Make Footwear Patterns*

# WWW.SNEAKERFACTORY.NET
## How Shoes are Made

## Written and Edited by
## Wade and Andrea Motawi

## ask_a_shoe_dog@sneakerfactory.net

## Dear Readers,

This book was written to educate, inform, and inspire the next generation of shoe designers, shoe developers, shoemakers, and footwear entrepreneurs! Our goal is to help prepare people for fulfilling careers in the world of shoes!

## Enjoy!

## Special thanks to:

Andrea, Alex & Erik, Karim, Halla, Mom & Dad, Dave, Alfredo, Jason, David, Lizzie, Johnson, Steve, Lenny, Bernie, Simon, Ben, Chad, The Mint Project.

Thanks to all my working friends in the USA, China, Hong Kong, Korea, Taiwan and Europe.

# How Shoes are Made

**WADE MOTAWI**

# HOW SHOES ARE MADE

# HOW SHOES ARE MADE

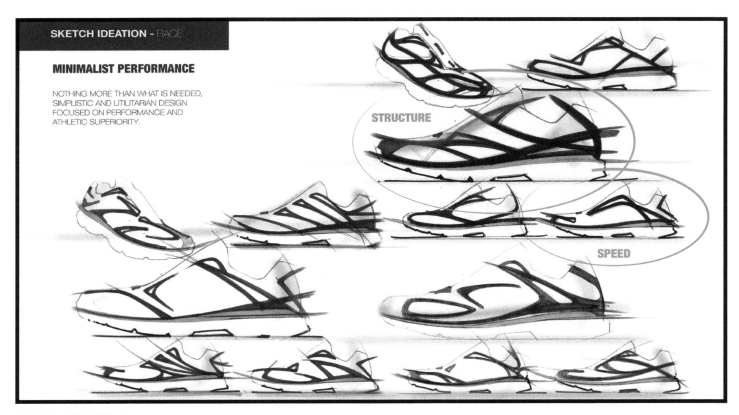

**MINIMALIST PERFORMANCE**

NOTHING MORE THAN WHAT IS NEEDED,
SIMPLISTIC AND UTILITARIAN DESIGN
FOCUSED ON PERFORMANCE AND
ATHLETIC SUPERIORITY.

STRUCTURE

SPEED

## CHAPTER 1

# THE SHOE DESIGN PROCESS

Most likely, the hardest part of making a new sneaker is trying to figure out what a 14-year-old in New York City or Peoria wants to wear on their feet.

The shoe designer has help to solve this mystery. Before the pencil is touched to paper, or the computer drawing program is opened, a team is already hard at work setting the creative direction for the design.

The process often begins with a disappointing sales report, a competitors catalog, or a new contract with an athlete. The product line manager will work with the designer to create a design brief for the shoe project.

## The design brief

How does the shoe design process actually work? Does a brilliant young shoe designer just create the new Air Jordan 24, or the Adidas Power Boost shoe design out of thin air? Not really, our shoe designer cannot do it all alone.

Our brilliant young shoe designer is just one part of a team of professionals that may include the Product Line Manager (PLM), Product Manager (PM), Footwear Developer, Pattern Maker, and Design Engineers.

The design brief is the document the entire team will use to create the new shoe. It is the instruction sheet and road map the product team will follow as they create the shoe. The design brief has information that each of our team members will need to get the job done right and to make the shoe a success. It is often submitted to the company's management for review before a project starts. With the manager's approval, the design brief becomes a written record of the shoe development team's goals for the project.

## Who makes the design brief?

There are no rules for this process; every company has their process. In many companies, the shoe design brief is a collaboration. The product manager is usually tasked with creating the brief, but he may meet with the designers or his design manager to collect style ideas. The PM should also be talking to his sales manager and sales reps for any price information or market intelligence about competitors.

Research is critical! The design team needs to know what's happening in the marketplace. Will your design be a mass market "me too" shoe, or will your design be a shocking revolution?

This research may show you need a new manufacturing process, or you need better prices, or maybe a new color or material palette.

## Two types of design briefs

A design brief can be a 1-page document, a 20-page report, or a pasted-up concept board. The format I have used has the design brief broken down into two styles.

The first brief being the demographic brief. This covers the target price, users' demographics, market competitors, and technical details. This brief asks and answers the questions: who is this for and what should it do?

The second brief is the visual design brief. It will detail the stylistic direction for the shoe. The visual brief will include photos of other shoes, cars, clothing, or anything the PM and designer can think of to help set the style or explain specific design details. In some cases, if the shoe is for a pro athlete, you may be inspired by the athlete's style or something they like.

This information should all be in the designer's mind when pen hits the paper. The first step is to make the rough concept drawings. Just get the idea first. Once the design direction has been set, the designer may create a CAD drawing to refine the concept.

## The demographic brief
### Price, Demographics, Competitors and Technical Details

What is the function of this shoe?
Running, basketball, snowboarding, tennis, bowling, logging, casual, or fashion?

Does the shoe have a special feature?
Thick midsole, thin midsole, fat tongue, no tongue, etc?

Who will wear this shoe?
Men, women, a new professional athlete, mall rats?

What retail price is planned for the finished shoe?
Price point, mid-range, deluxe or high end?

When will it arrive in stores?
Spring, Summer, Winter, Fall, or Holiday selling seasons?

What is the silhouette?
Ultra-low, low-cut, mid-cut, high-top?

What is the target environment for these shoes?
Forest, office, desert, track, high school, mountains?

What trends are up and coming?
Neon, earth tone, transparent, plaid?

What countries will sell this shoe?
USA, Canada, China, Europe, Australia?

What materials should be used?
High-tech synthetic or classic leather?

Is there a competitor's item doing well?

How many different colorways are required?

Are your engineers working on some new technology?

Is there a plan for import duty?

Are there existing outsole molds that can be or must be used?

Is there a particular new design element or material to try on this new shoe?

# The visual design brief

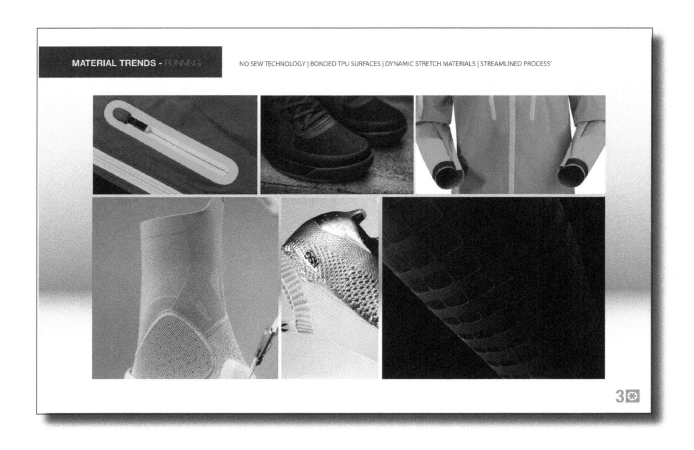

MATERIAL TRENDS - RUNNING — NO SEW TECHNOLOGY | BONDED TPU SURFACES | DYNAMIC STRETCH MATERIALS | STREAMLINED PROCESS'

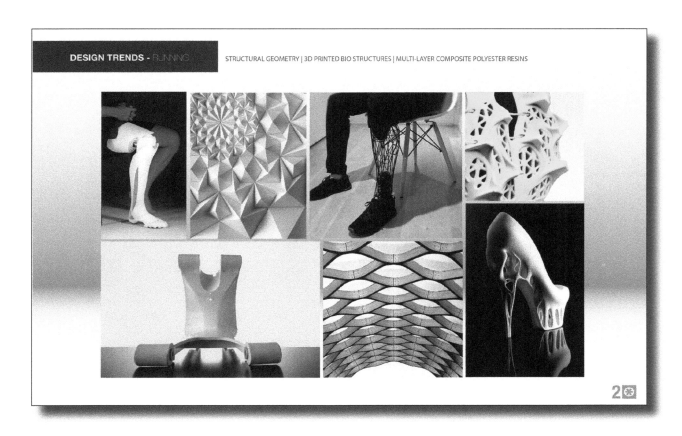

DESIGN TRENDS - RUNNING — STRUCTURAL GEOMETRY | 3D PRINTED BIO STRUCTURES | MULTI-LAYER COMPOSITE POLYESTER RESINS

# Drawing shoes

There is no right or wrong way to draw shoe designs. Every shoe designer will have a different way to put the shoe design down on paper. Of course, there are some who don't use paper at all!

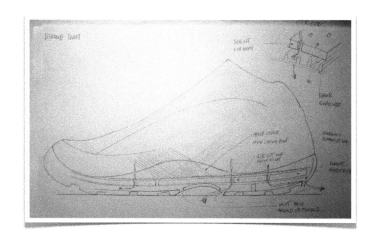

The goal of a shoe drawing is to communicate your idea of how the shoe will look or work. The drawing or sketch is also a tool for you to explore and develop your ideas. It's okay to mark up 100 sheets if that last sheet is a great design! It's okay to draw all week so that you get to the one great design on Friday afternoon.

As a shoe designer, your drawings can be for different purposes. Is it a styling drawing for a high fashion shoe? This drawing would be all about the colors and materials with little attention to the exact proportion or construction details. Conversely, if you are working on a high-tech running shoe, outdoor shoe, or soccer shoe, your drawing will need to be more accurate to describe the technical details. An accurate, well-proportioned shoe drawing will be much closer to the final product and can save you some future headaches if you can see potential flaws in the shoe drawing now.

Your first shoe "design" may not be a shoe at all. If the brief calls for a unique feature, your starting point may be just that detail.

Your new design may be focused on a particular logo element made of high tech material. Spend some time working on what you do know about the new design, and the other details may fall into place.

You may also need a break before you start. How can that be? I've seen designers collect all the information for a new project, organize the data, study the problem, then set the project aside for a few days. Doing this will allow your mind to work on the project and make some connections subconsciously.

Those notes may lead to a sketch of a design detail or a new way to construct the shoe. Perhaps a new ventilation system?

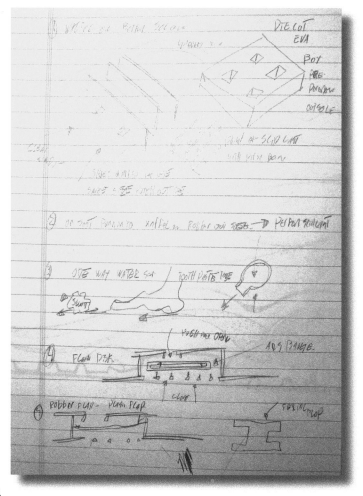

4

## Getting started

So, how do you get started drawing shoe designs? Yes, we are in the modern computer age, but even today most shoe designers begin with a pen and pencil. I have found a small stack of thin 8.5" x 11" paper is a great place to start. Thin paper so you can see your underlay. A small metal clip to hold the sheets together as you sketch. Whatever pencil you like, I like to use both wooden and mechanical depending on what I'm doing. I will often start with the mechanical pencil to draw lighter lines, then darken in the shoe design with the fat wooden pencil once I'm more confident with the design.

Other tools you may want are a set of french curves to make flowing smooth lines and a circle or oval template for other details like eyelets or logos. You could make a template of your company's logo to speed up sketching.

First, you need to start with a well-proportioned side profile. Go online, grab a magazine or catalog, measure or eyeball a shoe you have on hand. Use your phone camera to get a good side profile. Many times I've seen a young designer make a great looking dynamic drawing that looks nothing like a real shoe. How sad they are when the samples come back and look nothing like that fantastic drawing.

I take my side profile and clip it into my drawing pad under the first page, then go to work. At this point, go fast, break the design down into parts if it helps, toe cap, side panel, eyestay, heel counter. Each page should be just 5 minutes. I will darken in the parts I like, then pull a page off the bottom stack, redraw the parts I like, then draw in new ideas for the parts I do not like. In an hour you can make 10 pages, lay them out, then recombine elements you like again.

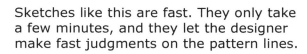
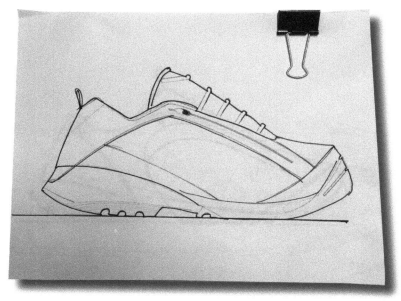

Sketches like this are fast. They only take a few minutes, and they let the designer make fast judgments on the pattern lines.

The key is speed! The pencil can lead you to a few new ideas. Just draw, if it sucks... move on.

A set of drawings should be done in just an hour or two.

Explore a theme...move on. FAST!

How can you apply the logos in new ways? Try a new design direction.

Experiment with different top lines, toe boxes, and logo applications.

From here, I will make one drawing, darken the lines, then photograph or scan it to pull the lines into Adobe Illustrator or another drawing program. Adobe Illustrator is the drawing program of choice. Once you have the drawing converted into a live vector format it's easy to adjust, pull, bend, and tweak outsole lines.

I like to use a set of simple templates as underlays. With the outline roughed in, you can spend your time on patterns and features. With the proportion correct, your design drawing will look closer to what the real shoe will look like.

You can make a set for your project in just a few minutes. Low-top, midsole, whatever you need.

## Hand drawing and CAD

Computer drawing programs are an important tool for the shoe designer. While the shoe designer may be able to close his or her eyes and imagine what the shoe will look like, the old fashioned sales manager or sales rep may not have the same abilities.

A quick rendering is a way to communicate to others what your shoe will look like before the time, effort, and expense is spent making the samples. The advantage of the computer rendering is that it can be done fast and changed even faster. Once the sketch is approved, a nice color rendering can be made in under an hour.

Starting with a hand sketch, a quick photo with your phone or scanner will get your underlay into the computer. If your drawing is carefully inked with dark lines many drawing programs will build the line art for you.

In this case, the automatic function would require more clean up than just drawing the lines. For a shoe like this, I like to start from the bottom of the outsole and work my way up, tracing part-by-part then sending each to the back layer of the drawings as I make the next part.

You don't need to waste time drawing the shape of the parts that overlap.

Once the main lines are drawn, the trim feature deletes the lines hidden from view. The hand sketch is now a click-able coloring book drawing ready for some rendering effects.

At this point, I like to add some color, laces, and hardware. Adding stitching is easy! I use the offset path function. Set the offset to negative -1.5mm, this will give you the inside line. Then, use your stroke tool to make a dashed line. With stitching, the drawing now looks like a shoe!

There are many techniques you can use to make your line art look more like a real shoe. I'm going to list a few of my favorite commands in Adobe Illustrator™ used to render this shoe.

1. Use the swatch fill tool to simulate leather. A photo of suede in this case. A photo of some 3D air mesh completes the upper.

2. Use the offset path tool to create stitching. If the drawing is to scale a -1.5mm offset, set with 1pt line weight. Make a dashed line with the stroke command.

3. Add a small drop shadow to the stitching.

4. To give the cut parts a 3D effect, I use the inner glow effect to darken the edges of the cut panels. Set color to black, 100% opacity, experiment with the blur to get the effect you like.

5. Use the fill swatch to add some extra texture on top of the midsole parts. Copy the part and change the fill to your texture for an overlay.

6. Use gradient fill on the metal hardware and then add a small drop shadow.

7. Use the fill swatch to make colored laces.

# Hunting

## Shoe design tools

Any photo from a magazine or the internet can be your base for an underlay. Here I've taken an image into Adobe Photoshop™ and used the find edges command to expose the silhouette.

From here it is easy to draw the line art and add stitch lines.

Once the underlay is built out, it is easy to create different models or colorways.

To add the camo patterns, use the clipping mask feature or the textured fill. To add depth, the inner glow command is used. To add the highlights, a gradient fill overlay was made with the opacity set to 20%.

**Military**

**WORK**

**Hunting**

## Color renderings

For this rendering, a fine grain, pebble leather pattern fill is added. White air mesh is also filled in using the swatch function. The laces, linings, and midsole all get some texture treatment. Shadows are added by use of the inner glow function.

Once you have a correctly detailed drawing, you can set up an entire product line in just a few minutes.

14

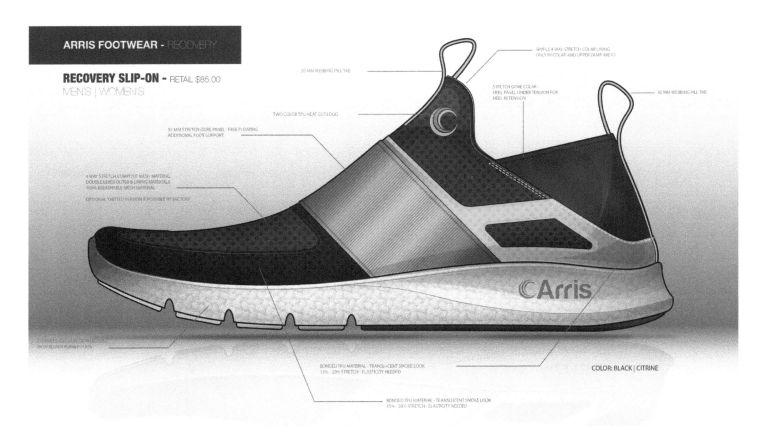

ARRIS FOOTWEAR - RECOVERY

**RECOVERY SLIP-ON -** RETAIL $85.00
MEN'S | WOMEN'S

SIMPLE 4 WAY STRETCH COLAR LINING
ONLY IN COLAR AND UPPER VAMP AREAS

20 MM WEBBING PILL TAB

STRETCH GORE COLAR -
HEEL PANEL UNDER TENSION FOR
HEEL RETENSION

20 MM WEBBING PILL TAB

TWO COLOR TPU HEAT CUT LOGO

55 MM STRETCH GORE PANEL - FREE FLOATING
ADDITIONAL FOOT SUPPORT

4 WAY STRETCH COMPOSIT MESH MATERIAL
DOUBLE LEYER OUTUR & LINING MATERIALS
100% BREATHABLE MESH MATERIAL

OPTIONAL KNITTED VERSION IF POSSIBLE BY FACTORY

BONDED TPU MATERIAL - TRANSLUCENT SMOKE LOOK
15% - 20% STRETCH - ELASTICITY NEEDED

COLOR: BLACK | CITRINE

BONDED TPU MATERIAL - TRANSLUCENT SMOKE LOOK
15% - 20% STRETCH - ELASTICITY NEEDED

## Color up your product line

High-quality color renderings are critical for decision making. Investors and sales managers will need to see exactly how the shoes look.

There is still a place for hand-drawn renderings. While a little old-fashioned, a hand rendering is another way to communicate your design with a different energy.

Starting with an inked underlay, apply the color in quick strokes, make a second pass around the edges to define contours. White colored pencil or white out paint is used to add highlights.

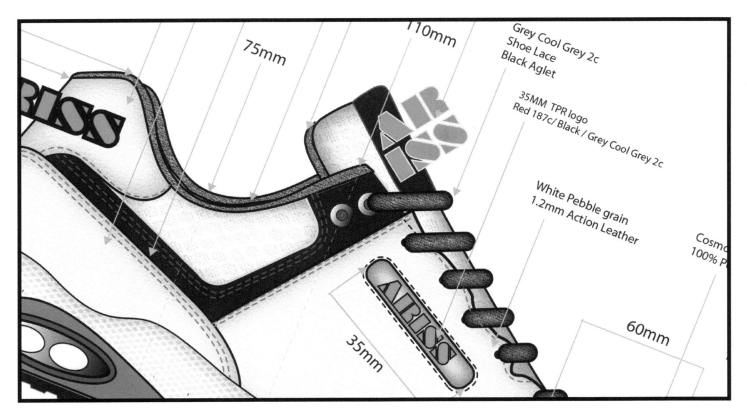

## CHAPTER 2

# FOOTWEAR SPECIFICATION DRAWINGS

Once the design concept has been selected and refined, it is time to turn the drawings into a new sneaker. This is when the footwear developer joins the designer to move the project forward.

The developer is an experienced technician that will transform the drawings into instructions for the factory. The development phase starts with a drawing and ends months later with a sample in the salesman's hands.

## The tech pack

Together, the designer and developer will create a detailed "tech pack" or a set of specification drawings or "specs." These drawings and documents detail every part of the sneaker from the upper, to the outsole bottom. The specifications include the name of each part, the material, supplier, thickness, and color.

The spec includes the shoe last information, logo art, design details, emboss effects, etc. The spec may also include sample shoes, material swatches, photos, or any other notes to help build the samples. The spec may be e-mailed, sent by courier service, or hand carried by the developer to the factory. At this point in the process, the developer is now responsible for getting the sample sneakers built.

# A complete spec drawing

Lateral View (outside of the shoe)
Medial View (inside of the shoe)
Heel View (view from the back)
Tongue View (showing any logo art)
Vamp View (looking down on the toe)
Detail views of any small plastic parts
Material map of the upper

Color map of the first sample color-way.
Outsole Side Profile
Outsole Bottom View
Outsole Top Net View
Detailed view of injection parts
Cross section view of the sole
Texture map showing the surface details
Color map showing future plans for color breaks

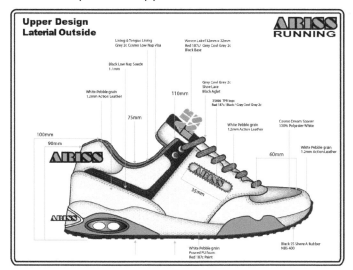

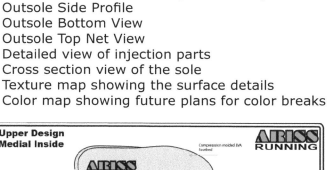

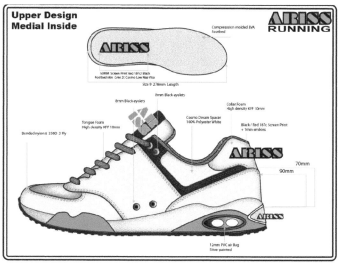

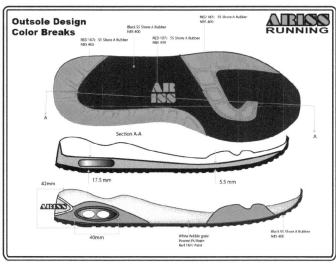

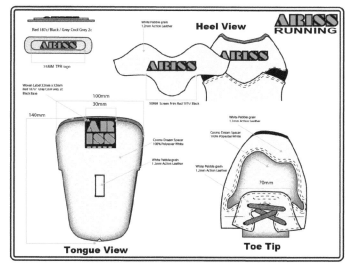

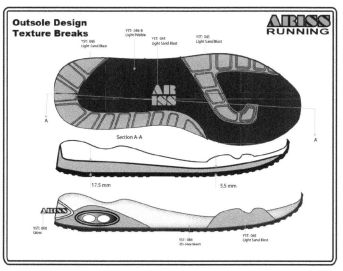

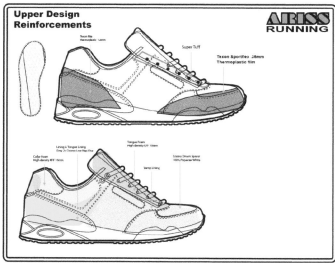

# Upper Design
# Lateral Outside

ARISS
RUNNING
Lining & Tongue Lining
Grey 2c Cosmo Low Nap Visa
Woven Label 32mm x 32mm
Red 187c/ Grey Cool Grey 2c
Black Base
Black Low Nap Suede
1.1mm
Grey Cool Grey 2c
Shoe Lace
Black Aglet
White Pebble grain
1.2mm Action Leather
110mm
35MM TPR logo
Red 187c/ Black / Grey Cool Grey 2c
75mm
White Pebble grain
1.2mm Action Leather
Cosmo Dream Spacer
100% Polyester White
100mm
90mm
White Pebble grain
1.2mm Action Leather
60mm
ARISS
35mm
White Pebble grain
Poured PU foam
Red 187c Paint
Black 55 Shore A Rubber
NBS 400


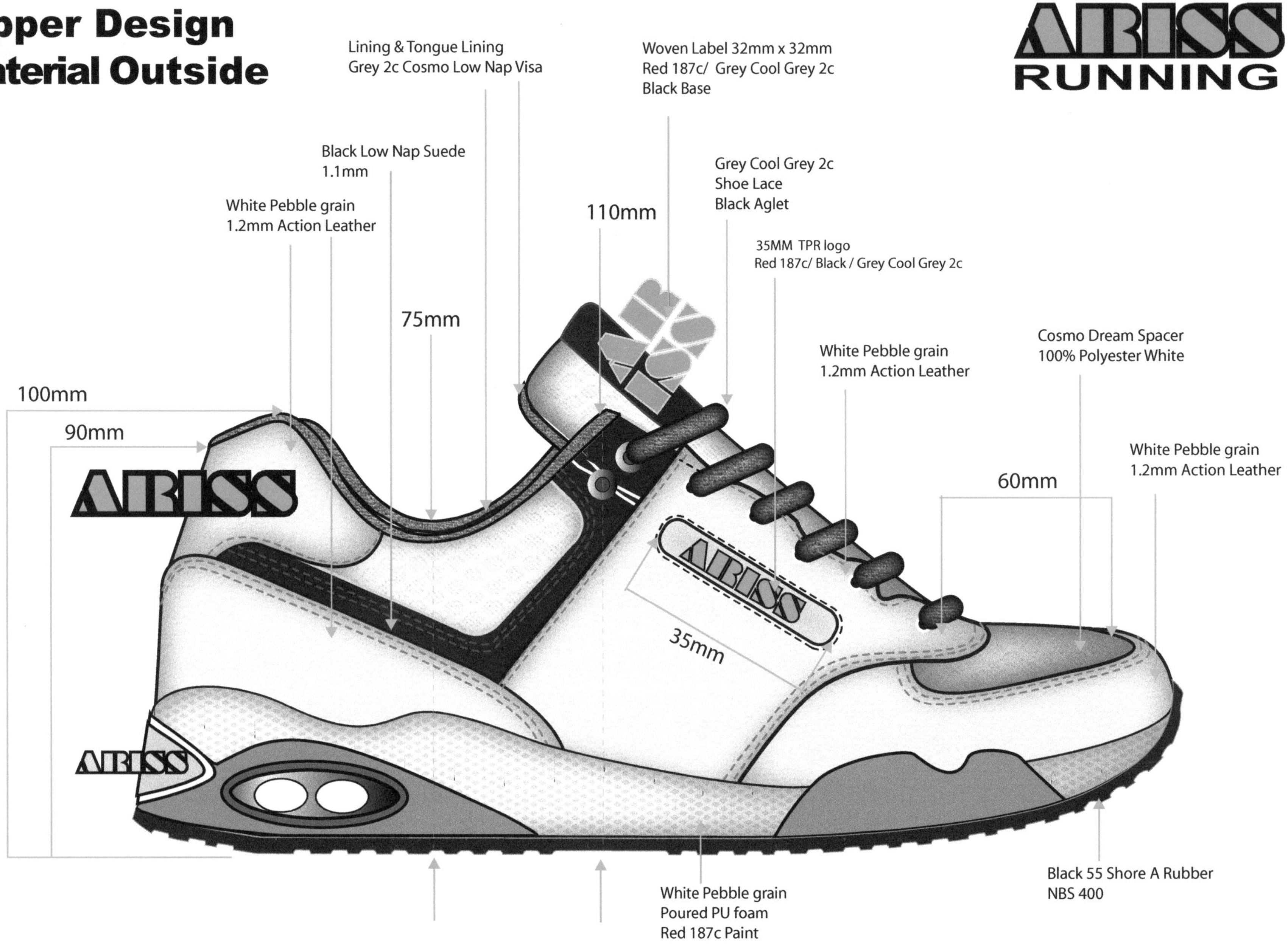

This drawing shows the Lateral view (or outside of the shoe) and Vamp view and the Footbed. Put as much detail as you can into these drawings. Remember a photo is worth more than 1000 words. If the technician in China does not speak English these details will truly help.

**Upper Design
Medial Inside**

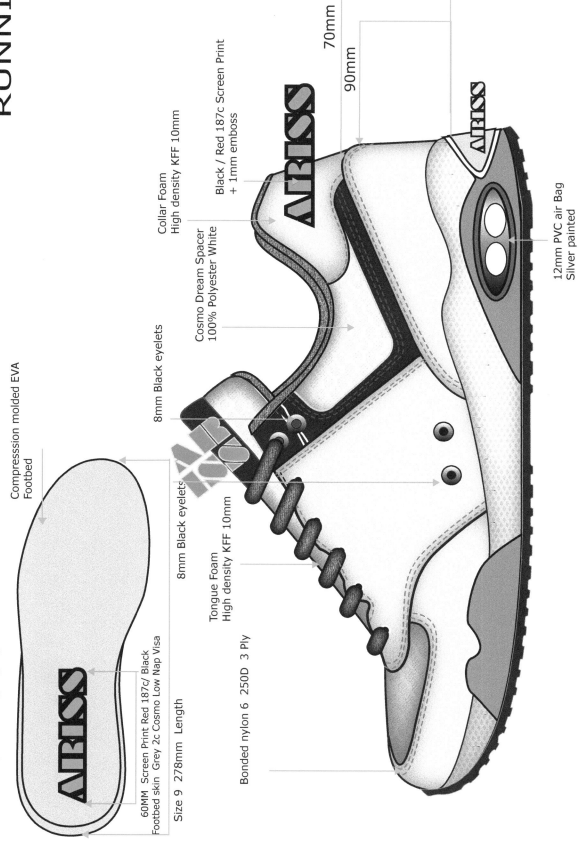

Compresssion molded EVA
Footbed

Collar Foam
High density KFF 10mm

Black / Red 187c Screen Print
+ 1mm emboss

Cosmo Dream Spacer
100% Polyester White

70mm

90mm

12mm PVC air Bag
Silver painted

8mm Black eyelets

8mm Black eyelets

Tongue Foam
High density KFF 10mm

Bonded nylon 6  250D  3 Ply

60MM  Screen Print Red 187c/ Black
Footbed skin  Grey 2c Cosmo Low Nap Visa

Size 9  278mm  Length

20

This is the Medial side or (inside) view of the shoe. Also show the tongue view and heel view of the design. If you can, try to list the logo dimensions.

# Outsole Design
# Color Breaks

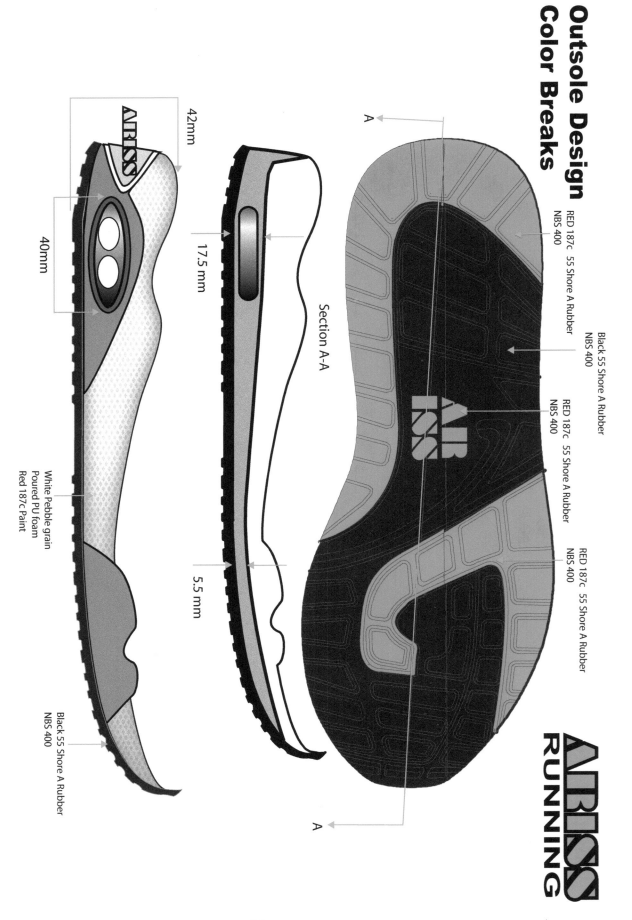

This drawing shows the outsole in color so the factory can see the logos and the designers idea for the color breaks. The color breaks must be tooled into the mold.

**AIRISS RUNNING**

42mm

40mm

17.5 mm

5.5 mm

Section A-A

A

A

White Pebble grain
Poured PU foam
Red 187c Paint

Black 55 Shore A Rubber
NBS 400

RED 187c   55 Shore A Rubber
NBS 400

Black 55 Shore A Rubber
NBS 400

RED 187c   55 Shore A Rubber
NBS 400

RED 187c   55 Shore A Rubber
NBS 400

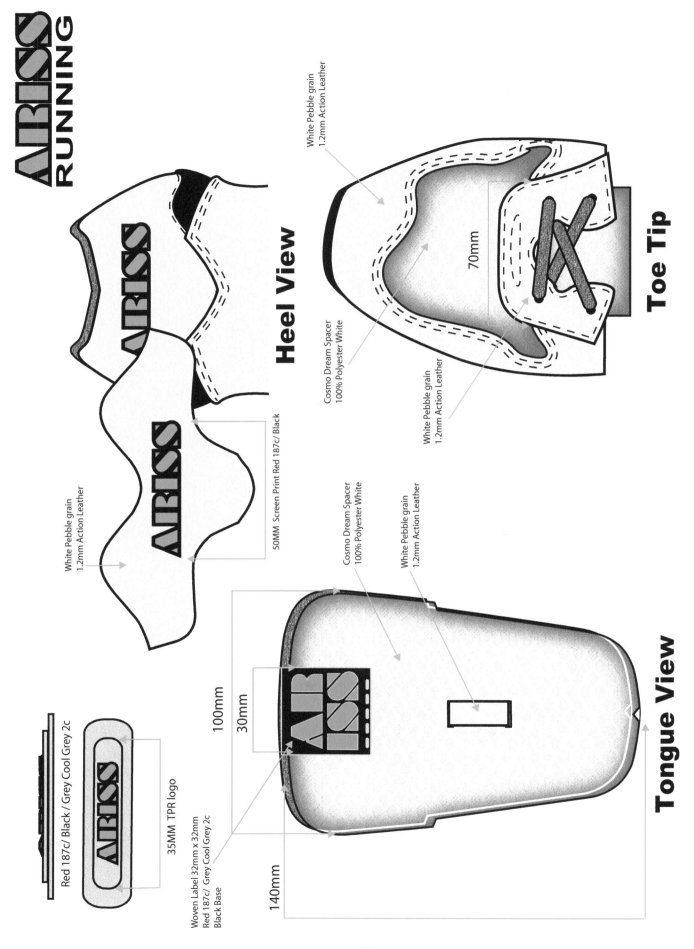

**RUNNING**

**Heel View**

White Pebble grain
1.2mm Action Leather

50MM Screen Print Red 187c/ Black

White Pebble grain
1.2mm Action Leather

White Pebble grain
1.2mm Action Leather

Cosmo Dream Spacer
100% Polyester White

White Pebble grain
1.2mm Action Leather

70mm

**Toe Tip**

Red 187c/ Black / Grey Cool Grey 2c

35MM TPR logo

Woven Label 32mm x 32mm
Red 187c/ Grey Cool Grey 2c
Black Base

100mm

30mm

140mm

Cosmo Dream Spacer
100% Polyester White

White Pebble grain
1.2mm Action Leather

**Tongue View**

This drawing shows the design details of the upper, molded logos, heel view, toe view and tongue view.

# Outsole Design
## Texture Breaks

This drawing shows the outsole textures for the tooling.

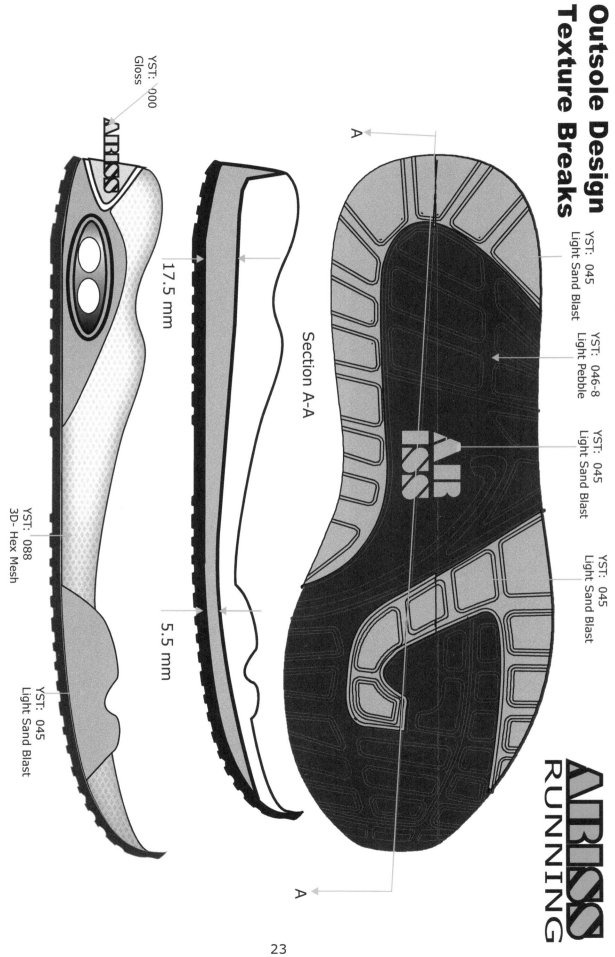

YST: 045
Light Sand Blast

YST: 046-8
Light Pebble

YST: 045
Light Sand Blast

YST: 045
Light Sand Blast

YST: 000
Gloss

YST: 088
3D- Hex Mesh

YST: 045
Light Sand Blast

17.5 mm

5.5 mm

Section A-A

A

A

AIRISS
RUNNING

# Upper Design
# Reinforcements

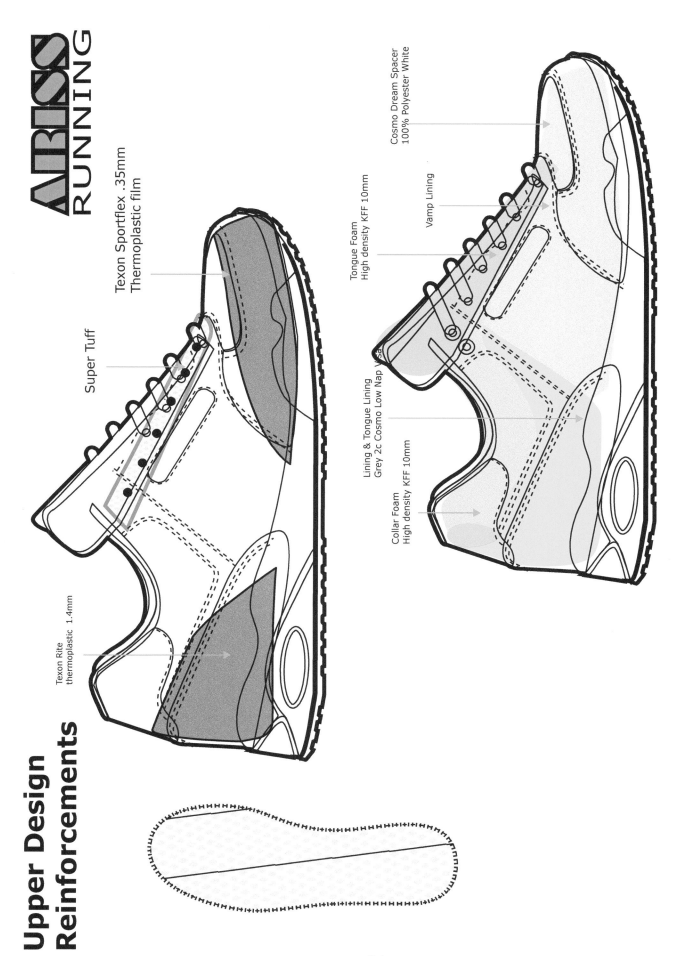

Texon Sportflex .35mm
Thermoplastic film

Super Tuff

Texon Rite
thermoplastic 1.4mm

Cosmo Dream Spacer
100% Polyester White

Tongue Foam
High density KFF 10mm

Vamp Lining

Lining & Tongue Lining
Grey 2c Cosmo Low Nap White

Collar Foam
High density KFF 10mm

24

Add any details to show the factory what internal construction you want in your new design.

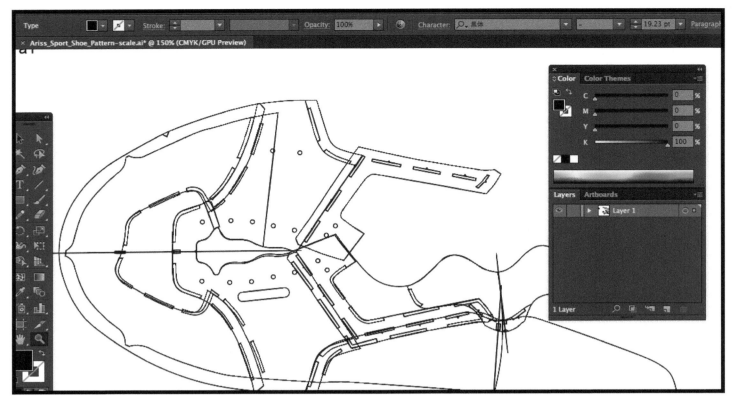

# CHAPTER 3

# MAKING FOOTWEAR PATTERNS

Once the shoe design is complete, the factory pattern maker or pattern master takes over. The pattern master transfers the designer's side profile, heel, and vamp drawings to make a "shell pattern" of the shoe. The shell pattern is what a one-piece seamless upper would look like. It is a blank, flat pattern, matched to the surface of the last. Once the shoe design is transferred to the shell pattern, the pattern master has the shape of each pattern part.

The pattern masters' skill makes a shoe come to life. Pattern masters work hard to follow the designer's drawings, but they also make adjustments so that the pattern parts fit together. After the shell pattern is drawn, it is hand cut from cardstock.

## The pattern makers challenge

The pattern masters' next task is to examine the shape of the last. If it is a familiar last, the pattern master may already have the shell pattern on file, and it's a simple task to mark the throat opening and the shoe collar height.

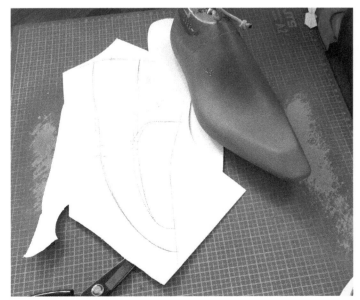

If the last is new, the pattern maker may "tape" the last so he can create the shell pattern. To tape the last, the pattern maker will cover half the last with layers of masking tape, then carefully cut the tape along the center line of the last and along the bottom edge. At this stage, the pattern master can draw the shoe design on the tape. Once the tape is peeled from the last and flattened, you have the pattern!

Now the pattern can be redrawn in a computer and cut out of heavy paper. As a designer, always ask for the flat pattern of a new design. When you make corrections, it's easy to review the sample shoe and mark the corrections on the paper pattern. It's fast and easy to scan your corrections and email them to the factory, rather than FedEx the shoe to China.

To the right is the pattern maker with the flat paper pattern. From this flat pattern, each shoe part can be created.

The paper pattern can be made by hand or by machine. There are many footwear CAD systems that can automatically transform a 3D design into a flat 2D pattern. These 3D systems can also grade the pattern to make sizes and calculate the material consumption for costing.

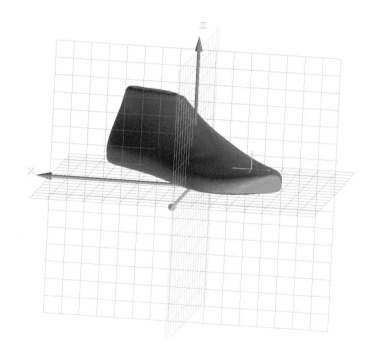

## What is the difference between a shoe designer and a pattern maker?

A shoe designer is responsible for all aspects of shoe design. The designer must consider the styling, materials, colors, customers, price, trends and product performance. The pattern maker, while crucial to the entire operation, is solely responsible for creating a beautifully proportioned pattern that fits tight to the last.

Does a footwear designer need to know how to make patterns? In my experience, a shoe designer does not need to know how to make footwear patterns. It's important that the shoe designer can read, work with, and adjust the patterns, but the creation of the new pattern is best left to the pattern master.

## Footwear construction and lasting
As the pattern master works to create the pattern, he must consider the lasting technique or the construction process required for the shoe. Each shoe type will demand a different construction depending on the stiffness, price, performance, and style. The upper pattern will need to reflect these choices.

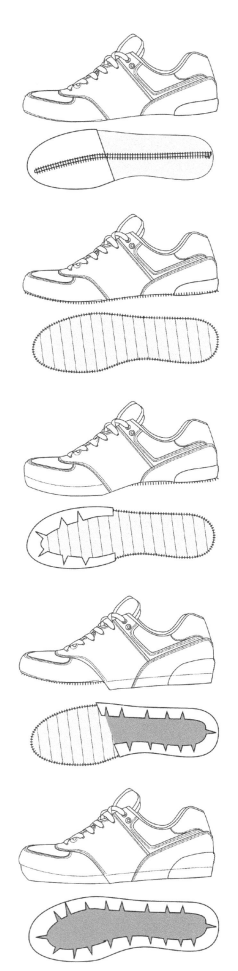

## Slip lasting

Slip lasting is commonly used to make flexible and lightweight shoes for running or racing. The upper materials, usually mesh or PU leather, are patterned to meet in the middle of the shoe's last bottom. Once the sides are joined, the upper will be steam-heated, and the last will be inserted while the shoe is laced up tight. The upper is then cooled, causing the material to tighten on the last before the outsole is attached.

## Strobel lasting

Strobel, slip, force, or California lasting is the most common shoe construction for casual and athletic shoes. Once the upper is complete, a "sock" or bottom material is added to "close" the bottom of the upper. This material does not stretch and is marked to help the assembler keep the upper straight on the last. As with slip lasting, the upper is heated and slipped onto the last; then it will be cooled, causing the material to tighten on the last. A machine assist may be used to make sure the last heel is down tight inside the upper.

## Combination lasting

The combination last is used to ensure the toe of a shoe is correctly formed to the last. For a shoe with a smooth, solid toe cap, the strobel sock may be attached to the inner lining, and a lasting "skirt" may be left on the toe cap pattern part. Once the upper is lasted, a second machine operation is used to pull the toe pattern part down tight. This shoe construction is often used for light hiking boots and basketball shoes with smooth leather toe tips. Toe lasting allows the leather to be shaped with a lasting machine.

The combination last may also be used to make a lightweight shoe stiffer. In this case, the forefoot is formed by strobel, while the rear of the shoe is board lasted. This allows the shoe to have a shank or stiffer board in the rear of the shoe. A machine is used to "heel last" the upper, while the waist area may be pulled by hand with a pair of lasting pliers. You will find this shoe construction on "support" shoes and light hikers.

## Board lasting

Board lasting is a very common process used to make military, hunting, hiking boots, or any shoe requiring a stiff bottom (and usually a steel toe). The open upper is placed into a lasting machine that grips the upper and pulls it down onto the last. The last has been prepared with a paperboard or plastic lasting board inside and may also have a metal shank inside. In one operation, the lasting machine pulls the upper tight around the last and injects glue between the upper and the lasting board. A heel lasting machine and some hand pulling will complete the operation before the outsole is attached. Women's fashion shoes are also made by board lasting, but a delicate touch is required by the lasting machine operator to avoid damaging the uppers. Handmade shoes are almost always board lasted by hand.

Board lasting shoe construction is also used to make the classic running shoe with a sheet cut EVA midsole. This shoe requires the upper to be tucked far under the edge because the flat midsole does not hide where the upper meets the midsole.

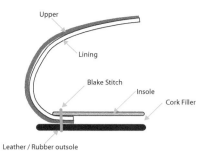

## Blake construction

Blake construction is used to make flexible leather shoes. The Blake construction starts with a board lasted upper. The sole is glued in place and with the last removed, the upper is sewn directly through the outsole unit. The outsole may be leather or rubber and may have a groove molded into its surface to guide the blake stitch. You will find blake construction on weltless leather dress shoes, moccasins, and boat shoes. Blake construction is not waterproof.

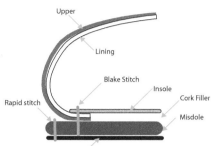

## Blake/Rapid construction

Similar to the standard blake construction, but with a "rapid" perimeter stitch attaching the outsole. The outsole covers the blake stitching. This allows for a thicker sole and is easier to re-sole. The extra layer may be made of rubber to make the shoe more durable.

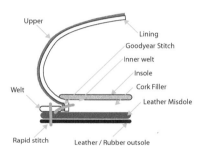

## Goodyear welt construction

The Goodyear welt is often used to make waterproof soles. The stitch that attaches the sole to the shoe runs around the outside edge and does not make stitch holes in the upper. The upper is sewn to the welts which attach to the insole and the outsole. During assembly, the welts are attached first by a horizontal "Goodyear" stitch, named for the inventor of the stitching machine, Charles Goodyear Jr. (also the son of the famous rubber inventor, Charles Goodyear Sr.). The Goodyear welt construction method is ideal for heavy duty boots used for hiking or service.

## Norwegian storm welt construction

The Norwegian welt construction is similar to the Goodyear welt construction method, but the upper is turned outside and is sandwiched between the outer welt and the outsole. Norwegian storm welt is used to make the heaviest waterproof boots. It is difficult to achieve and is found almost exclusively in the workshops of Italian boot makers.

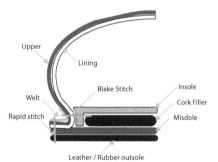

## Stitch down Veldtschoen welt construction

Again, the Veldtschoen welt is related to the Goodyear and Norwegian welt constructions. In this case, an inner welt, or rapid stitch line through the midsole is paired with a second rapid stitch that attaches the outsole. The outsole is attached after the first welt, and the bottom stitch is protected by the outsole.

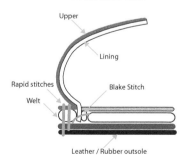

## Bologna construction

Developed in Italy, and used primarily for dress or fashion shoes, the Bologna construction creates a smooth, comfortable shoe. The shoe lining is joined into a sock, fitting the last tightly. The leather upper is then attached to the sole via the Blake stitching method. The Bologna shoe construction method is ideal for making clean and flexible shoes.

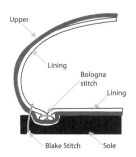

## A simple pattern

1. Heel patch or Mustache
2. Heel counter reinforcement
3. Collar padding:
4. Heel lining
5. Tongue lining
6. Tongue padding
7. Tongue logo panel
8. Tongue face
9. Quarter panel medial side
10. Quarter panel lateral side
11. Eyestay reinforcement medial
12. Eyestay reinforcement lateral
13. Quarter panel lining medial side
14. Quarter panel lining lateral side
15. Toe cap / Vamp
16. Toe puff reinforcement
17. Vamp / Toe cap lining

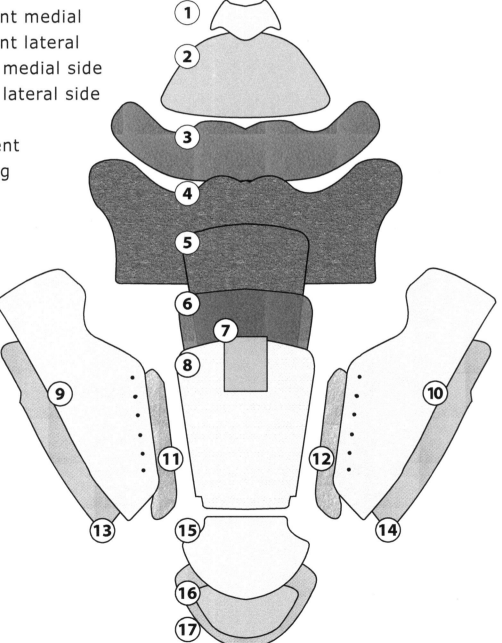

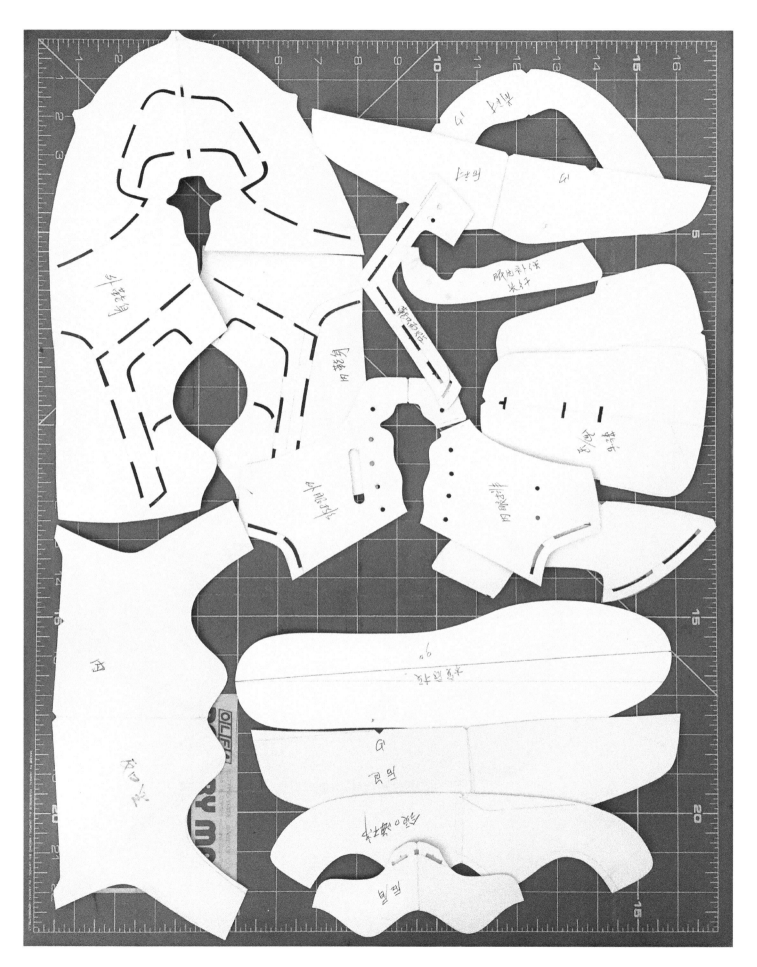

30

## Flat patterns

Here is a "flat" pattern. All the lines and shapes are 100% to scale. When you get your new samples, ask for the flat pattern so you can mark corrections.

These can be emailed to you or cut paper can be sent with the shoes.

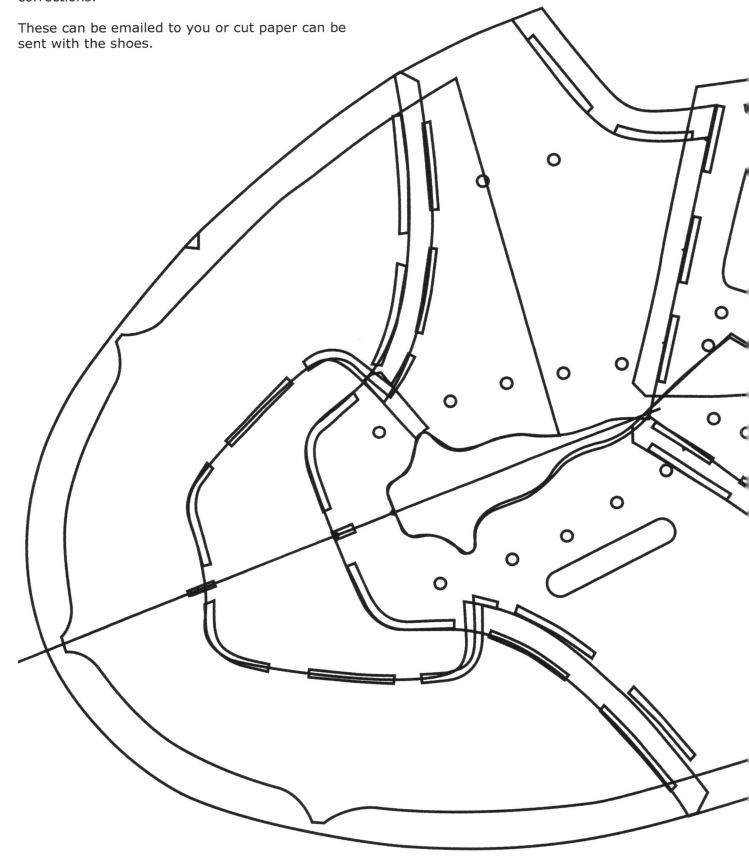

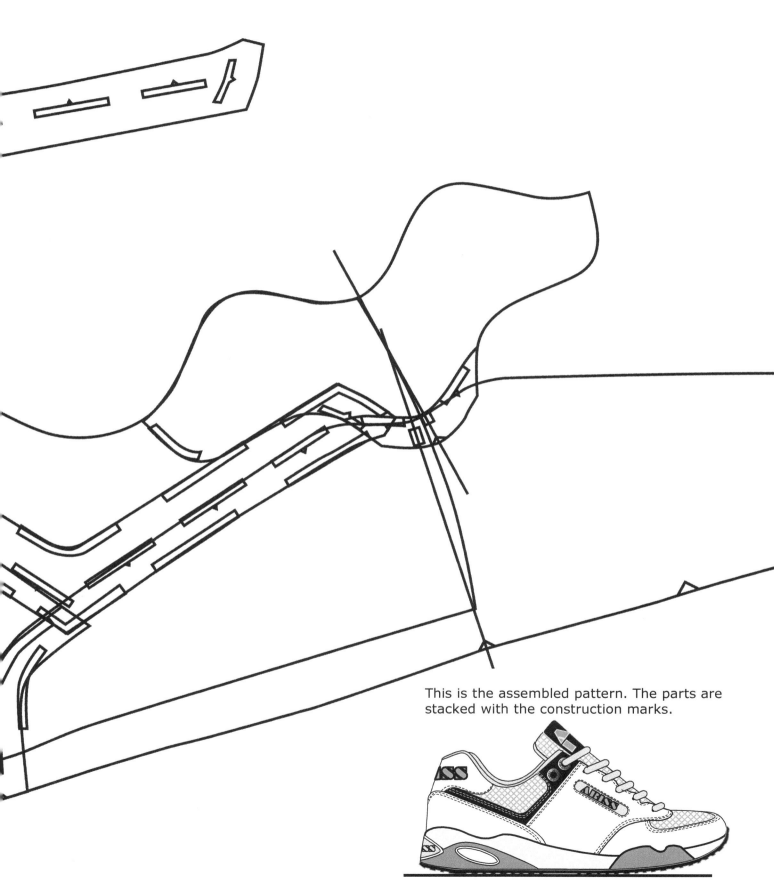

This is the assembled pattern. The parts are stacked with the construction marks.

32

## How to make a shoe pattern

Making a shoe pattern is not hard! If you have time and patience, you can make a shoe pattern with a few common tools. The techniques are simple, the process is easy, but the skills to create a beautiful, well proportioned, mechanically sound shoe pattern take years to perfect!

Here is a list of the tools you will need:

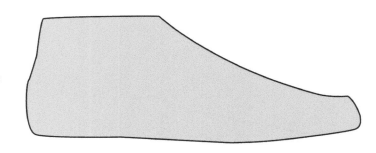

1. A shoe last
2. 1/2 inch masking tape
3. A sharp X-Acto™ knife or hobby knife
4. Pens and pencils
5. A small, flexible steel ruler
6. Stiff paper

## Tape the shoe last

To make a new shoe pattern you will need to create a flat, 2D shape that echoes the 3D surface. A pattern maker will apply tape to the last, then peel off the tape and flatten it to create the shell pattern.

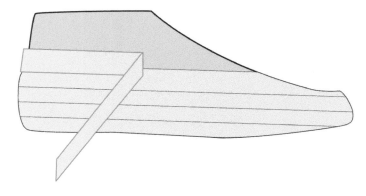

The tape should be layered in two different directions so the pattern stays together when you are ready to peel the tape off the last. You will start on the lateral, or outside of the shoe last.

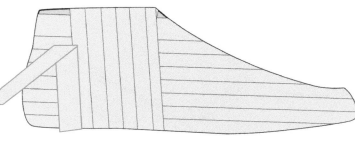

First, lay the tape lengthwise down the lateral side of the last, starting at the bottom. Follow with tape running top to bottom, start in the middle and work back to the heel of the last.

Next, return to the middle and work forward. The tape should be firmly flattened to the last as you go to make a smooth accurate surface.

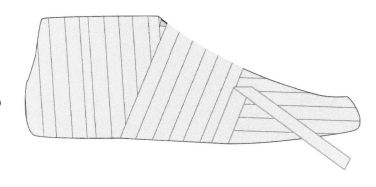

Finally, run a stripe of tape down the center of the last from the top of the instep down to the toe. Do the same down the heel of the last.

Make sure the tape wraps around the bottom edge of the last. You will need this edge, as it will become the bottom edge of your shoe pattern.

With your last prepared, you can follow any of three procedures for making your pattern. You can cut the tape pattern in half and flatten it down on paper stock, then draw the pattern on the flat shell pattern. Second, you can draw the pattern on the tape before you flatten the shell pattern. Third, is to draw the pattern on the last, then using a knife, remove and flatten the pattern parts one by one.

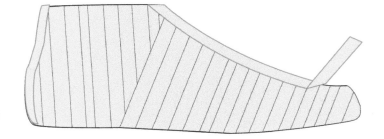

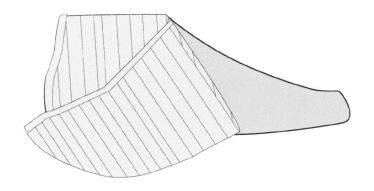

# Flattening the shell pattern

With a sharp knife, carefully cut the tape starting at the top and cutting down the center line to the toe, repeat at the heel. Trim the bottom and top edge of the last to make a clean shell. Starting at the toe, slowly remove the tape in one large piece.

Starting in the middle of the taped pattern, lay the tape on a stiff piece of cardstock. Carefully press the tape to the paper, work slowly to make sure there are no wrinkles. As you work out from the center, you will need to make a few small relief cuts along the bottom edge as the pattern flattens. This is normal.

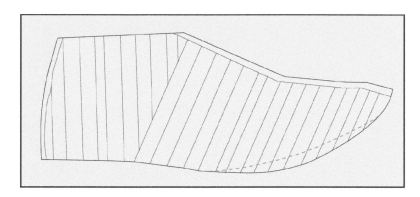

Once you flatten both sides of the tape from the last, you will see there is a difference. The medial side of the pattern requires a little more material than the lateral side. The difference can be marked on the shell. If your shoe design is asymmetrical, you will need to draw two different patterns.

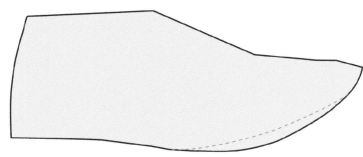

Once the tape is flattened to the cardstock, cut out the shape and then transfer it to a new clean sheet of cardstock. Keep the original for your shell pattern library, if you use the same last again you will be ready.

The last bottom pattern can be created by the same tape process or simply traced onto cardstock. You will need the last bottom pattern to make the footbed and for the Strobel bottom.

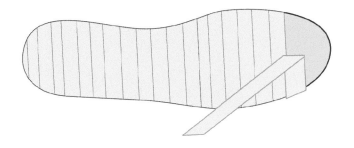

34

## Marking the shell pattern

While every shoe pattern is different, there are some starting points to follow when marking out any pattern. These starting points are based on the length of the last.

## Last length

The last length is measured from the heel to the toe tip.

## Vamp length

For a standard athletic shoe, the vamp length is about 30% of the last length. For men's dress shoes, the vamp length may be 50% of the last length.

## Back height

The back height is 20% of the last length plus 15mm.

## Collar line height

The collar line height is set at 25% of the last bottom length.

## Throat opening

The top eyelet is located 25% of the last length. Measure from the vamp point. The top of the eyestay is located at a height of 25% of the last length plus 25mm. Measure from the bottom of the pattern.

## Collar opening

The opening is defined by lines connecting the back height, throat opening top line, and a point on the last bottom located 25% of the last length when measuring forward from the heel.

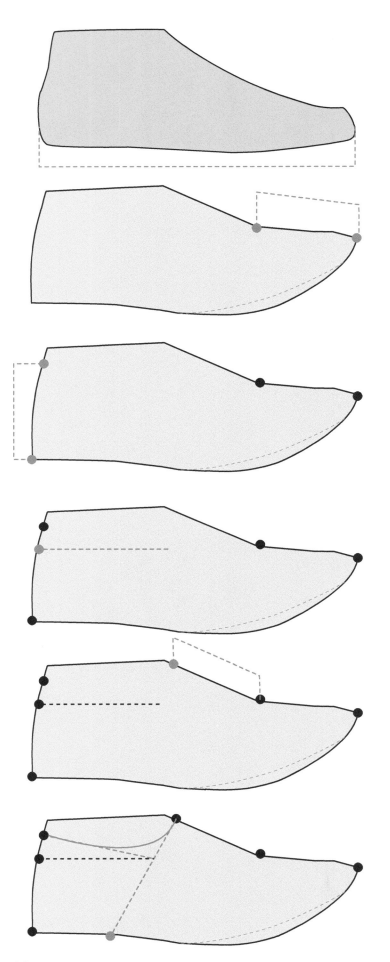

35

## Throat width

Throat width is 10mm at the first eyelet position, tapering to 0 at the top eyelet position. The throat width dimension will increase as the tongue foam increases.

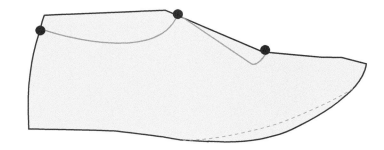

## Mudguard

The mudguard top line is not measured, it is set by locating the line just past the apex of the last's contour.

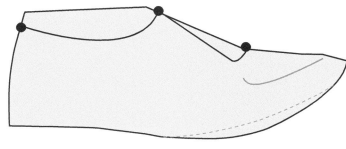

## Tongue dimensions & location

The tongue length is set to 25mm beyond the top of the eyestay. The tongue is attached to the upper 20mm below the vamp line. The standard tongue, based on a men's size nine shoe, will be 25mm wide at the base and 45mm wide at the top.

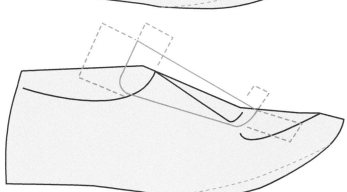

## Marking the pattern

Once the key points are marked, the details of the design can be drawn.

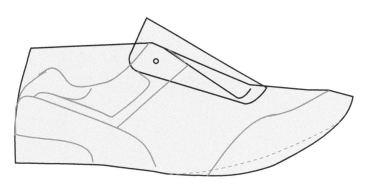

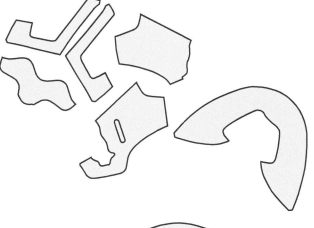

## Pattern overlaps and lasting allowances

If you are working from the flat pattern, then the pattern overlaps and lasting allowances will need to be added by hand. They can be drawn, then cut out.

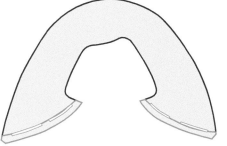

## Men's pattern grade

| | | | | | | | | | | | | | | | | | | | |
|---|---|---|---|---|---|---|---|---|---|---|---|---|---|---|---|---|---|---|---|
| USA | 6 | 6.5 | 7 | 7.5 | 8 | 8.5 | 9 | 9.5 | 10 | 10.5 | 11 | 11.5 | 12 | 12.5 | 13 | 13.5 | 14 | 14.5 | 15 |
| UK | 5.5 | 6 | 6.5 | 7 | 7.5 | 8 | 8.5 | 9 | 9.5 | 10 | 10.5 | 11 | 11.5 | 12 | 12.5 | 13 | 13.5 | 14 | 14.5 |
| Euro | 38 | 38.5 | 39 | 40 | 41 | 42 | 43 | 43.5 | 44 | 44.5 | 45 | 45.5 | 46 | 46.5 | 47 | 47.5 | 48 | 48.5 | 49 |
| Japan | 24 | 24.5 | 25 | 25.5 | 26 | 26.5 | 27 | 27.5 | 28 | 28.5 | 29 | 29.5 | 30 | 30.5 | 31 | 31.5 | 32 | 32.5 | 33 |
| Bottom Length | 252 | 256 | 260 | 264 | 268 | 272 | 276 | 280 | 284 | 288 | 292 | 296 | 300 | 304 | 308 | 312 | 316 | 320 | 324 |
| A Vamp Length | 76 | 77 | 78 | 79 | 80 | 82 | 83 | 84 | 85 | 86 | 88 | 89 | 90 | 91 | 92 | 94 | 95 | 96 | 97 |
| B Throat Height | 88 | 89 | 90 | 91 | 92 | 93 | 94 | 95 | 96 | 97 | 98 | 99 | 100 | 101 | 102 | 103 | 104 | 105 | 106 |
| C Back Height | 60 | 61 | 62 | 63 | 64 | 64 | 65 | 66 | 67 | 68 | 68 | 69 | 70 | 71 | 72 | 72 | 73 | 74 | 75 |
| D Collar Height | 50 | 51 | 52 | 53 | 54 | 54 | 55 | 56 | 57 | 58 | 58 | 59 | 60 | 61 | 62 | 62 | 63 | 64 | 65 |

## Women's pattern grade

| | | | | | | | | | | | | | | | |
|---|---|---|---|---|---|---|---|---|---|---|---|---|---|---|---|
| USA | 5 | 5.5 | 6 | 6.5 | 7 | 7.5 | 8 | 8.5 | 9 | 9.5 | 10 | 10.5 | 11 | 11.5 | 12 |
| UK | 2.5 | 3 | 3.5 | 4 | 4.5 | 5 | 5.5 | 6 | 6.5 | 7 | 7.5 | 8 | 8.5 | 9 | 9.5 |
| Euro | 35 | 35.5 | 36 | 37 | 37.5 | 38 | 38.5 | 39 | 40 | 41 | 42 | 43 | 44 | 45 | 46.5 |
| Japan | 21 | 21.5 | 22 | 22.5 | 23 | 23.5 | 24 | 24.5 | 25 | 25.5 | 26 | 27 | 28 | 29 | 30 |
| Bottom Length | 234 | 238 | 242 | 246 | 250 | 254 | 258 | 262 | 266 | 270 | 274 | 278 | 282 | 286 | 290 |
| A Vamp Length | 70 | 71 | 73 | 74 | 75 | 76 | 77 | 79 | 80 | 81 | 82 | 83 | 85 | 86 | 87 |
| B Throat Height | 84 | 85 | 86 | 87 | 88 | 89 | 90 | 91 | 92 | 93 | 94 | 95 | 96 | 97 | 98 |
| C Back Height | 57 | 58 | 58 | 59 | 60 | 61 | 62 | 63 | 64 | 65 | 65 | 66 | 66 | 67 | 68 |
| D Collar Height | 47 | 48 | 48 | 49 | 50 | 51 | 52 | 52 | 53 | 54 | 55 | 56 | 56 | 57 | 58 |

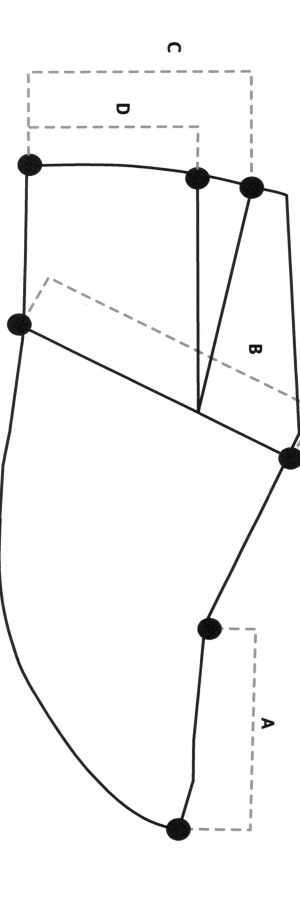

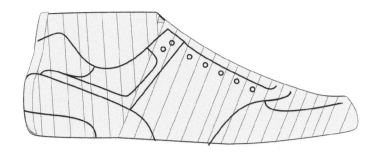

## Drawing on the last

Once the shoe last is covered with tape, it is time to start marking the shoe pattern. With a steel ruler, mark the center line of the last from the instep to the toe tip and down the heel. Once the center line is marked, it's easy to mark the other key dimensions.

Follow the same process used for marking the flat pattern: create marks for the back height, vamp length, tongue, and collar. With the key points marked, while the tape is still on the last, you can avoid making some basic mistakes.

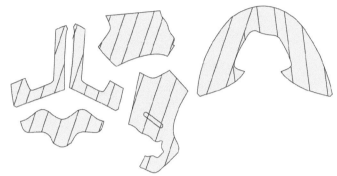

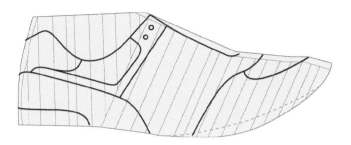

## Flatten the pattern

Once you have the pattern drawing you can flatten the entire pattern or cut out each part and flatten the parts individually. Once the pattern parts have been flattened, the lasting allowances and pattern overlaps can be added by hand.

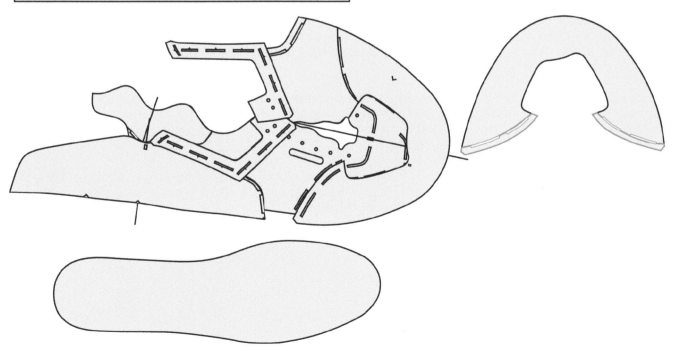

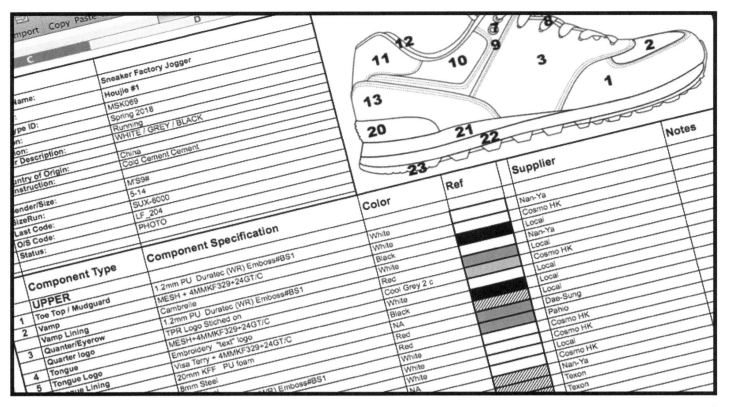

# CHAPTER 4

# SHOE SPECIFICATION DOCUMENTS

The designer's spec drawings will allow the pattern master to create the 3D pattern of the shoe. The designer's outsole drawings allow the factory's mold shop to get started drawing the blueprints for the tooling needed to make any molded parts.

From the designer's drawings a detailed product specification or "Spec Sheet" will be created. In a small company, the designer may complete the spec sheets him/herself, in larger firms a developer will work with the designer to create the detailed spec. Here is a spec sheet made on a spreadsheet. Large shoe brands will have a database system to hold the data; smaller shoe companies will create the spec sheet in Microsoft Excel.

The spec sheet lists each shoe part, the material code number or thickness, color, and supplier. At this point, many of the details may be missing, that's okay. It is the developer's job to fill in the blanks as the shoe development continues. Once the spec is sent to the factory, the factory development staff will work with the developer and designers to complete it.

The spec is an important document. When it is time for production, the approved spec sheet will become the contract with the factory. The spec sheet is also a living document. As the shoe is developed, the spec sheet is changed and updated onward to production.

This is a very simple spec sheet for a basic item. A high-tech sneaker or snowboard boot spec may have many pages. For a complicated item, the supplier part number of the materials must also be included.

| | | | | | |
|---|---|---|---|---|---|
| Project Name: | Ariss Jogger | | | | |
| Factory: | Houjie #1 | | | | |
| Prototype ID: | ARJ-001 | | | | |
| Season: | Spring 2018 | | | | |
| Division: | Running | | | | |
| Color Description: | WHITE / RED / BLACK | | | | |
| Country of Origin: | China | | | | |
| Construction: | Cold Cement Cement | | | | |
| | Board Lasted | | | | |
| Gender/Size: | M'S9# | | | | |
| SizeRun: | 5-14 | | | | |
| Last Code: | SUX-6000 | | | | |
| O/S Code: | LF_204 | | | | |
| Status: | Photo Sample | | | | |

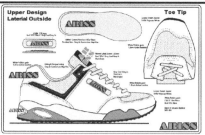
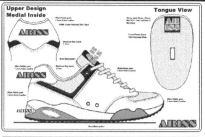
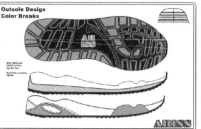
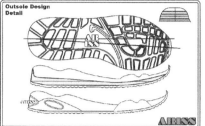

| | Component Type | Component Specification | White/Red/Black | Color | Supplier |
|---|---|---|---|---|---|
| | **UPPER** | | | | |
| 10 | Toe Top / Mudguard | 1.2mm White Pebble grain Action Leather | White | | Nan-Ya Tanning |
| 20 | Vamp | Cosmo Dream Spacer 100% Polyester | White | | Cosmo HK |
| 30 | Vamp Lining | Cosmo Dream Spacer 100% Polyester | White | | Local |
| 40 | Quanter/Eyerow | 1.2mm White Pebble grain Action Leather | White | | Nan-Ya Tanning |
| 50 | Quarter logo | TPR Logo "Ariss" | Red 187c/Black/Grey 2c | | Local |
| 60 | Tongue | Cosmo Dream Spacer 100% Polyester | Cool Grey 2 c | | Cosmo HK |
| 70 | Tongue Lace keeper | 1.2mm White Pebble grain Action Leather | White | | Nan-Ya Tanning |
| 80 | Tongue Logo | 32mm x 32mm Woven Label Stacked "Ariss" | Red 187c/Black/Grey 2c | | Local |
| 90 | Tongue Lining | Visa Terry + 4MMKF329+24GT/C | Cool Grey 2 c | | Local |
| 100 | Tongue Foam | 20mm KFF PU foam | NA | | Local |
| 110 | Lace Eyelets | 8mm Steel | Black | | Dae-Sung |
| 120 | Medial Vents | 8mm Steel | Black | | Dae-Sung |
| 130 | Shoe Lace | 8mm Oval | Cool Grey 2 c | | Pahio |
| 140 | Collar Underlay | Low Nap Suede 1.2mm | Black | | Local |
| 150 | Collar Panel | Cosmo Dream Spacer 100% Polyester | White | | Cosmo HK |
| 160 | Heel Logo | Print + Emboss 55mm ARISS | Red/Black | | Local |
| 170 | Heel Lining | Visa Terry + 4MMKF329+24GT/C | NA | | Cosmo HK |
| 180 | Heel Counter | 1.2mm White Pebble grain Action Leather | NA | | Nan-Ya Tanning |
| 190 | Internal Heel Counter | Texon Rite thermoplastic 1.4mm | NA | | Texon |
| 200 | Internal Toe Puff | Texon Sportflex .35mm thermoplastic film | NA | | Texon |
| 210 | Eyerow Reinforcement | Super Tuff | NA | | Local |
| 220 | Upper Thread | bonded nylon 6 250D 3 Ply | Matching | | Coats or A&E |
| | | | | | |
| | **OUTSOLE UNIT** | | | | |
| 230 | Midsole Wedge Top | Hot Press EVA Asker "C" 45-50 | White | | Local |
| 240 | Outsole | #1-44 NBS400 Shore "A" 65 +or-3 SG 1.1 +1.4 | Black | | CW Pressing |
| 250 | Outsole Color Break | NBS400 Shore "A" 65 +or-3 SG 1.1 +1.4 | Red | | CW Pressing |
| 260 | Outsole Logo | "ARISS" Logo NBS400 Shore "A" 65 +or-3 SG 1.1 +1.4 | Red | | CW Pressing |
| 270 | Outsole Tip Stitching | bonded nylon 6 850D 3 Ply | Red | | Coats or A&E |
| 280 | Insole Strobal | Texon T28 | White | | Texon |
| 290 | Footbed | Cold Pressed EVA Asker "C" 45 Standard Open Mold | Black | | Local |
| 300 | Foobed Skin | Cosmo Hex Weave | White | | Cosmo HK |
| 310 | Foobed Logo | Screen Print Logo "ARISS" 65mm Heat Transfer | Black / Red | | Local |
| 320 | Cement | Water based PU | Clear | | Nan-Pou |
| | | | | | |
| | **PACKING** | | | | |
| 330 | Inner Box | 2016 Box art E-Flue - White Back PVC skin | Red | | Lai-Wah |
| 340 | Out Carton | Brown | Brown | | Local |
| 350 | Tongue label | 3cm x 3cm White + Black Screen + Weld | Black / White | | Local |
| 360 | EEC label | 2cm x 2cm White + Black Print | Black / White | | Local |
| 370 | HangTag | 4-Color Print | Color | | Lai-Wah |
| 380 | Tag pin | White | White | | Local |
| 390 | Wrap Tissue | 10 gram 2 sheets | White | | Local |
| 400 | Toe Tissue | 10 gram 2 sheets | White | | Local |

# The spec sheet

The footwear specification sheet or simply "spec" sheet does a few things:

1. Tells the shoe factory the name of each part of your design.
2. Details what each shoe part is made of.
3. Tells the shoe factory what color every part is.
4. Tells who supplies each material to the shoe factory.

A detailed specification sheet is critical to your success. If you leave line items open with no details the factory developer will choose whatever they have inside the factory for these parts. This may be good or may be bad, but you may get an unexpected result.

You will also use the spec sheet to check the new samples that come in from the factory. It's important to review each sample with the spec sheet to make sure that the factory followed the specification sheet. It's good to highlight differences and ask the factory why they did not follow the spec sheet. Maybe they have a suggestion that's better than what you chose? In many cases, the factory developer or pattern maker will substitute a material they have on hand, and it may work better than your original specification.

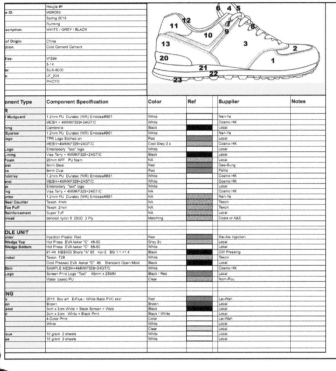

# Material maps

You should make a material map when first specifying an item the factory has not seen before. It's important for the shoe factory to know the terminology we are using.

Take a black-and-white drawing and give each piece a number. Make sure the numbers on your spec sheet match the drawings. This takes just a few minutes and can save you the hassle of a simple mistake. I like to count by 10's so I can add lines later if I need to. You can use letters to separate outsole parts.

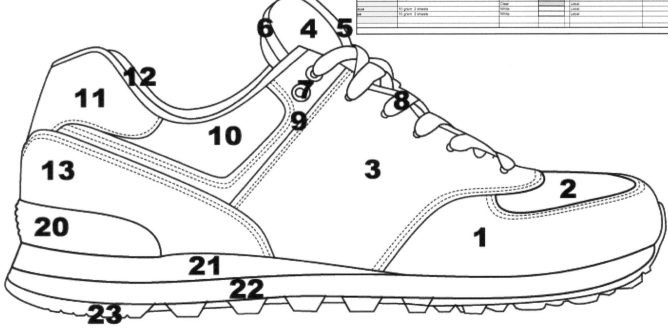

# Spec sheet header

Big companies will have a database system to manage spec sheets, but medium and small companies can manage just fine with Microsoft Excel or other spreadsheet programs.

The specification sheet header contains lots of key information the factory will need to keep your project organized and make the samples. Your header should include:

The development model year and season

The shoe factory name

Model name or number if it does have a name

Outsole tooling code numbers

Size run information

Designer or Developer's name

Last code number

Sample color information

The sample round

| Project Name: | Ariss Jogger |
|---|---|
| Factory: | Houjie #1 |
| Prototype ID: | ARJ-001 |
| Season: | Spring 2018 |
| Division: | Running |
| Color Description: | WHITE / RED / BLACK |
| Country of Origin: | China |
| Construction: | Cold Cement Cement |
| | Board Lasted |
| Gender/Size: | M'S9# |
| SizeRun: | 5-14 |
| Last Code: | SUX-6000 |
| O/S Code: | LF_204 |
| Status: | Photo Sample |

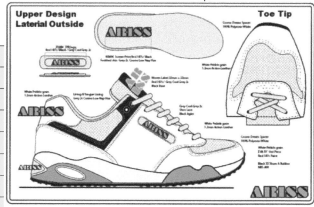

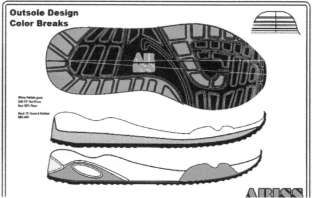

42

# Filling in the spec sheet

I like to break up the components of the shoe into several sections. The first section being the upper components of the shoe. Start with the front of the shoe and work backward. Then, list the inside lining components and the reinforcing components, all those pieces that you can't see inside the shoe like the vamp lining, collar lining, etc... In this section, you can also list things like the glue, collar foam density and thickness, and the thread type you want to use.

The bulk of the information on the spec sheet will include the names of the components and then what material you specified for each component. When detailing the shoe materials, list the name, the manufacturer, and the code number or the swatch book.

Depending on the material, list the thickness of the material, the emboss pattern, and the backing material.

| | Project Name: | Sneaker Factory Jogger |
| --- | --- | --- |
| | Factory: | Houjie #1 |
| | Prototype ID: | MBX069 |
| | Season: | Spring 2018 |
| | Division: | Running |
| | Color Description: | WHITE / GREY / BLACK |
| | Country of Origin: | China |
| | Construction: | Cold Cement Cement |
| | Gender/Size: | M'S99 |
| | Size/Run: | 5-14 |
| | Last Code: | SUX-6000 |
| | O/S Code: | LF_204 |
| | Status: | PHOTO |

# Let's look at this sample spec.

#1 is the Toe Cap.

The material thickness is 1.2mm. This material is PU (Polyurethane leather). The product name is "Duratec." In this case, it has (WR) water resistant treatment added to the backing layer. The material is available in many different surface patterns or "emboss patterns." In this case, emboss#BS1. The color is "White," the material manufacturer is "Nan-Ya."

If the material vendor is new to the factory, it is useful to add the factory contact information somewhere on your spec sheet.

| | Component Type | Component Specification | Color | Ref | Supplier |
| --- | --- | --- | --- | --- | --- |
| | **UPPER** | | | | |
| 1 | Toe Top / Mudguard | 1.2mm PU Duratec (WR) Emboss#BS1 | White | | Nan-Ya |
| 2 | Vamp | MESH + 4MMKF329+24GT/C | White | | Cosmo HK |
| | Vamp Lining | Cambrelle | Black | | Local |
| 3 | Quarter/Eyerow | 1.2mm PU Duratec (WR) Emboss#BS1 | White | | Nan-Ya |
| | Quarter logo | TPR Logo Stiched on | Red | | Local |
| 4 | Tongue | MESH+4MMKF329+24GT/C | Cool Grey 2 c | | Cosmo HK |
| 5 | Tongue Logo | Embroidery "text" logo | White | | Local |
| 6 | Tongue Lining | Visa Terry + 4MMKF329+24GT/C | Black | | Local |
| | Tongue Foam | 20mm KFF  PU foam | NA | | Local |
| 7 | Lace Eyelet | 8mm Steel | Red | | Dae-Sung |
| 8 | Shoe Lace | 8mm Oval | Red | | Pahio |
| 9 | Collar Underlay | 1.2mm PU Duratec (WR) Emboss#BS1 | White | | Cosmo HK |
| 10 | Collar Panel | MESH+4MMKF329+24GT/C | White | | Cosmo HK |
| 11 | Heel Logo | Embroidery "text" logo | White | | Local |
| 12 | Heel Lining | Visa Terry + 4MMKF329+24GT/C | NA | | Cosmo HK |

# Specing the outsole unit

The next section will call out the footwear outsole unit components. List the rubber parts, colors, and other details like the logo. You can also spec the following features:

Rubbers hardness (shore "A" scale)
The SG or specific gravity
Rubber color
Midsole material
Midsole hardness or durometer
Sockliner foam
Sockliner cover fabric

| | Project Name: | Sneaker Factory Jogger | | | | |
|---|---|---|---|---|---|---|
| | Factory: | Houjie #1 | | | | |
| | Prototype ID: | MSK089 | | | | |
| | Season: | Spring 2016 | | | | |
| | Division: | Running | | | | |
| | Color Description: | WHITE / GREY / BLACK | | | | |
| | Country of Origin: | China | | | | |
| | Construction: | Cold Cement Cement | | | | |
| | Gender/Size: | M 99# | | | | |
| | SizeRun: | 5-14 | | | | |
| | Last Code: | SUX-6000 | | | | |
| | O/B Code: | LF_204 | | | | |
| | Status: | PHOTO | | | | |

| | Component Type | Component Specification | Color | Ref | Supplier | Notes |
|---|---|---|---|---|---|---|
| | **UPPER** | | | | | |
| 1 | Toe Top / Mudguard | 1.2mm PU  Durabo (WR) Emboss#BS1 | White | | Nan-Ya | |
| 2 | Vamp | MESH + 4MMKF329+24GT/C | White | | Cosmo HK | |
| | Vamp Lining | Cambrelle | Black | | Local | |
| 3 | Quarter/Eyerow | 1.2mm PU  Durabo (WR) Emboss#BS1 | White | | Nan-Ya | |
| | Quarter logo | TPR Logo Stiched on | Red | | Local | |
| 4 | Tongue | MESH+4MMKF329+24GT/C | Cool Grey 2 c | | Cosmo HK | |
| 5 | Tongue Logo | Embroidery "text" logo | White | | Local | |
| 6 | Tongue Lining | Visa Terry + 4MMKF329+24GT/C | Black | | Local | |
| | Tongue Foam | 20mm KPF  PU foam | NA | | Local | |
| 7 | Lace Eyelet | 8mm Steel | Red | | Dae-Sung | |
| 8 | Shoe Lace | 8mm Oval | Red | | Local | |
| 9 | Collar Underlay | 1.2mm PU  Durabo (WR) Emboss#BS1 | White | | Cosmo HK | |
| 10 | Collar Panel | MESH+4MMKF329+24GT/C | White | | Cosmo HK | |
| 11 | Heel Logo | Embroidery "text" logo | White | | Local | |
| 12 | Heel Lining | Visa Terry + 4MMKF329+24GT/C | NA | | Local | |
| 13 | Heel Counter | 1.2mm PU  Durabo (WR) Emboss#BS1 | NA | | Nan-Ya | |
| | Internal Heel Counter | Texon 4mm | NA | | Texon | |
| | Internal Toe Puff | Texon 2mm | NA | | Texon | |
| | Eyerow Reinforcement | Super Tuff | NA | | Local | |
| | Upper Thread | bonded nylon 6  250D 3 Ply | Matching | | Coats or A&E | |
| | | | | | | |
| | **OUTSOLE UNIT** | | | | | |
| 20 | Heel Counter | Injection Plastic Red | Red | | Xie-Xie Injection | |
| 21 | Midsole Wedge Top | Hot Press  EVA Asker "C"  45-50 | Grey 2c | | Local | |
| 22 | Midsole Wedge Bottom | Hot Press  EVA Asker "C"  55-60 | White | | Local | |
| 23 | Outsole | #1-44  NBS400 Shore "A" 65  +or-3  SG 1.1 +1.4 | Black | | CW Pressing | |
| | Insole Strobal | Texon T28 | White | | Texon | |
| | Footbed | Cold Pressed EVA Asker "C"  45  Standard Open Mold | Black | | Local | |
| | Footbed Skin | SAMPLE MESH+4MMKF329+24GT/C | White | | Cosmo HK | |
| | Footbed Logo | Screen Print Logo "Text"  45mm x 25MM | Black / Red | | Local | |
| | Cement | Water based PU | Clear | | Nom-Pou | |
| | | | | | | |
| | **PACKING** | | | | | |
| | Inner Box | 2016 Box art  E-Flue - White Back PVC skin | Red | | Lai-Wah | |
| | Out Carton | Brown | Brown | | Local | |
| | Tongue label | 3cm x 3cm White + Black Screen + Weld | Black | | Local | |
| | EEC label | 2cm x 2cm  White + Black Print | Black / White | | Local | |
| | HangTag | 4-Color Print | Color | | Lai-Wah | |
| | Tag pin | White | White | | Local | |
| | Poly bag | | Clear | | Local | |
| | Wrap Tissue | 10 gram  2 sheets | White | | Local | |
| | Toe Tissue | 10 gram  2 sheets | White | | Local | |

# Let's look at this sample spec

#23 is the rubber outsole.
We can look at this spec and see the mold code number is #1-44, the rubber compound is an extra durable compound NBS400, the rubber hardness is measured in the "Shore A" scale. Shore "A" 65, we give the factory a range of +or- 3, the density is SG 1.1 +1.4

The midsole is hot pressed EVA with hardness measured in the Asker "C" scale 45-50

| | | | | | | |
|---|---|---|---|---|---|---|
| | **OUTSOLE UNIT** | | | | | |
| 20 | Heel Counter | Injection Plastic  Red | Red | | Xie-Xie Injection | |
| 21 | Midsole Wedge Top | Hot Press  EVA Asker "C"  45-50 | Grey 2c | | Local | |
| 22 | Midsole Wedge Bottom | Hot Press  EVA Asker "C"  55-60 | White | | Local | |
| 23 | Outsole | #1-44  NBS400 Shore "A" 65  +or-3  SG 1.1 +1.4 | Black | | CW Pressing | |
| | Insole Strobal | Texon  T28 | White | | Texon | |
| | Footbed | Cold Pressed EVA Asker "C"  45  Standard Open Mold | Black | | Local | |
| | Footbed Skin | SAMPLE MESH+4MMKF329+24GT/C | White | | Cosmo HK | |
| | Footbed Logo | Screen Print Logo "Text"  45mm x 25MM | Black / Red | | Local | |
| | Cement | Water based PU | Clear | | Nom-Pou | |

# Packing

Remember, everything you want to ship with your shoe must be included on the spec sheet.

The final section of the spec sheet should list any of the items that are not necessarily part of the shoe but are still part of the package.

For example the cardboard box, the tissue paper, tags, stuffing, extra shoelaces, if you have a keychain, or a user manual in a plastic bag. Anything like that should be included in the final section.

| | **PACKING** | | | | | |
|---|---|---|---|---|---|---|
| | Inner Box | 2016  Box art  E-Flue - White Back PVC skin | Red | | Lai-Wah | |
| | Out Carton | Brown | Brown | | Local | |
| | Tongue label | 3cm x 3cm White + Black Screen + Weld | Black | | Local | |
| | EEC label | 2cm x 2cm  White + Black Print | Black / White | | Local | |
| | HangTag | 4-Color Print | Color | | Lai-Wah | |
| | Tag pin | White | White | | Local | |
| | Poly bag | | Clear | | Local | |
| | Wrap Tissue | 10 gram  2 sheets | White | | Local | |
| | Toe Tissue | 10 gram  2 sheets | White | | Local | |

**CHAPTER 5**

# OUTSOLE TOOLING DESIGN

The outsole tooling for athletic shoes is the most complicated and most expensive piece of equipment required for production. The tooling comes in many different styles and configurations. Shoe outsoles are made from many different types of rubber, plastic, foam, leather, or fabric, each with tooling requirements and manufacturing technology.

While the designer is responsible for creating the general look and style of the outsole, it is the shoe factory's job to draw the final blueprints and make sure all the parts fit together correctly. In this chapter, we will review the common outsole styles and what kind of blueprint you will need to make tooling.

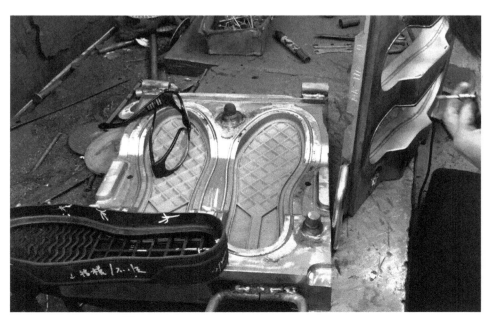

A mold shop making adjustments to a cupsole side wall mold.

Let's review the design requirements and tooling for rubber, plastic, and foam outsoles found in the modern athletic sports and casual shoes. The outsole design you select for your shoe is critical to its comfort, performance, and price. You will need to know the equipment requirements and unit price for each type of outsole design.

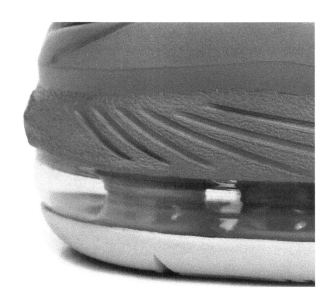

It's critical to understand the tooling and manufacturing requirements for each outsole type. If you are designing for Nike™, go ahead and design a complicated outsole with blow molded airbags, plastic injections, etc. the sky is the limit. $20,000 per size for tooling is no problem. If the production is a million pairs, then $150,000 for the tooling is no problem. However, if you are a start-up, strapped for cash, the tooling for a cupsole unit will cost $1,400 per size and is a more realistic choice.

Of course, performance matters. It's a bad idea to use a rubber cupsole for a running shoe or a huge airbag in a combat boot.

Basic Outsole Types: Rubber cupsole, cut and buff EVA wedge sole, combination cut and buff/cupsole, two-piece EVA rubber sole, vulcanized rubber sole, lightweight EVA outsole, EVA sole unit, injection molded EVA, injection molded plastic sole unit, blow molded airbag sole unit.

## Outsole Types

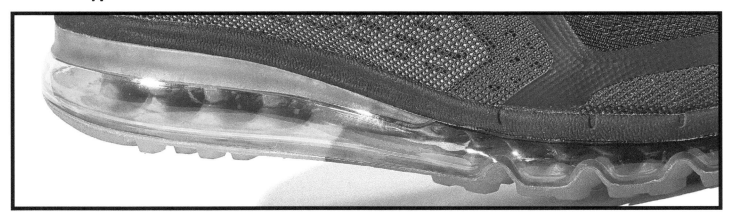

The airbag midsole is made by the blow molding process. The midsole starts out as a hot, semi-liquid plastic extrusion tube (called a parison). A steel mold clamps around the tube and the air is injected inside to fill the bag and inflate the shape to fill the mold. The tooling and machines are very expensive. The plastic can be tinted, and the bag top and bottom surfaces can be painted. In this case, the airbag is attached to an EVA tray that is then bonded to the shoe outsole by cold cement process. This type of sole unit is great for running and cross training. The airbag looks cool, but due to the blow molding process the plastic walls of the bag can be a little thick. This sole unit requires an EVA compression mold, rubber compression mold, and blow molds.
TOOLING:$$$$  UNIT PRICE:$$$$

## Compression Molded EVA or CMEVA

The standard two-part sole is made with lightweight CM EVA midsole, bonded to a rubber outsole. The EVA foam is expanded into blocks then cut down to fit into a mold. The mold is heated, causing the EVA to re-expand and fill the compression mold. The density and durometer are set by how much foam is compressed into the mold and the formula of the foam. More foam is harder and gives the sole design more definition. The midsole is bonded to the rubber in the stock fitting room before the unit meets the upper in assembly. This sole unit requires an EVA compression mold and a rubber compression mold.
TOOLING:$$  UNIT PRICE:$$

## Injection molded midsoles

Many firms have been experimenting with foamless injection molded midsoles. This shoe has a stiff moderating plate under the heel to keep the shoe stable. The midsole structure is likely made of nylon or TPU plastic. The rubber tread is attached by stock fitting. This sole unit requires an EVA compression mold for the midsole hidden inside, rubber compression mold for the tread, and injection molds for the midsole component.
TOOLING:$$$$  UNIT PRICE:$$$$

## Injection molded EVA

This running shoe uses an injection molded EVA midsole with rubber inserts. The injected midsole has a thicker, smoother skin than a compression molded EVA midsole. The injected EVA midsole has a more uniform density and better detail definition than the compression molded EVA. This unit is very light and very flexible but will wear quickly. The injection molded tooling has a high production rate, but the molds are over $3,000 per size and require an expensive machine. This sole unit requires an EVA injection mold and rubber compression mold.
TOOLING:$$$  UNIT PRICE:$$

47

## The EVA wedge

This classic die-cut EVA wedge midsole is bonded to a compression molded rubber bottom. The top wedge shape of the EVA is cut by pressing the EVA with a profile roller while a blade splits off the bottom layers. The white layer is buffed and bonded to the rubber bottom. All three parts are then buffed to create the angled side wall. This process is labor intensive but requires very little tooling. In fact, one bottom tool can be trimmed to make 4 to 6 sizes. This New Balance shoe requires a rubber compression tool.
TOOLING:$  UNIT PRICE:$

## Poured PU midsole

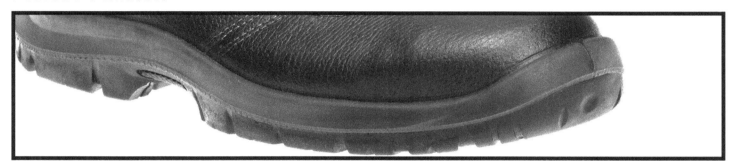

This shoe is made by PU foam direct attach. In this process, the upper is clamped into the top of a mold. The mold is filled in two shots: first, the sole is molded, the bottom cools in a few minutes then the second shot of lightweight PU will fill the space between the upper and bottom. The PU fuses directly to the upper. This sole requires a 2-part PU rubber injection mold AND a million dollar machine.
TOOLING:$$$  UNIT PRICE:$

## Classic airbag with PU midsole

This classic airbag shoe midsole is made by over-molding PU, but in this case, the airbag is clipped in the heel and exposed. The window is where the clamps hold the bag in place, and they stop the PU from covering the bag. The rubber sole is made by compression, the top of the black part is the mold's parting line. The yellow part with specs is the same PU part holding the airbag, but this area is masked off and painted. After the PU parts are cleaned and painted, they are bonded to the rubber parts by the stock fitting line. The toe channel stitching is done after assembly. This outsole requires a rubber compression tool, airbag mold and PU midsole mold.
TOOLING:$$  UNIT PRICE:$$

## 3/4 cup / cut and buff sole

This indoor soccer shoe is a combination cupsole and cut and buff. The rubber is pressed, then the EVA wedge is cemented in place. The EVA is then buffed down to match the rubber sidewall. This construction is more flexible and lighter than a standard rubber cupsole. This outsole requires a rubber compression mold.
TOOLING:$$  UNIT PRICE:$$

## Classic vulcanized outsole

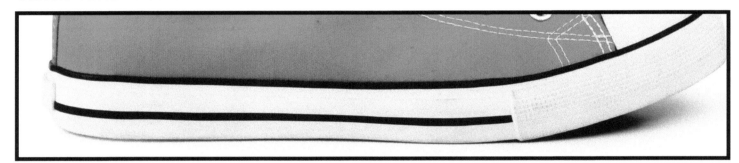

This outsole is standard vulcanized shoe construction. The sole bottom is bonded to the upper, and then striped rubber foxing tape wraps them both. After this assembly operation is done, the entire shoe is cooked to cure the rubber thus making the bonds permanent. This outsole requires a rubber compression mold for the bottom and a special vulcanizing production factory.
TOOLING:$  UNIT PRICE:$

## Injection molded outsole

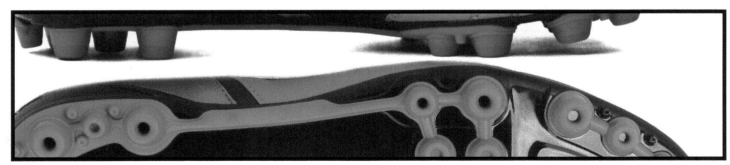

This soccer cleat outsole is made by the injection molding process. Cleated shoes for soccer, football, and baseball require stiff, supportive bottoms. Cleated shoe uppers are attached to the outsole by the cold cement process. The sole unit may be sewn to the upper after the cementing operation. This outsole requires a plastic injection mold. Complicated designs with several colors require an expensive mold, and simple designs require less expensive tooling. Cleats with metal spikes or inserts require over-molding or insert molding processes. This type of injection tooling requires a specialized injection molding factory.
TOOLING:$$-$$$$  UNIT PRICE:$ to $$$$

# Rubber cupsole

This is a classic cup shoe with a one-piece rubber cupsole. The white sidewall and black rubber are molded together in one operation. The mold has a middle plate allowing the parts to be formed separately. Before the rubber is fully cured, the middle plate is removed so the rubber colors can fuse together without a messy seam. The side logo is painted after molding. Inside, you will find a die-cut piece of EVA foam. The stitch groove is an undercut in the mold, but the stretchable rubber is easily removed after molding. The channel stitching is done after assembly. This requires only a rubber compression mold.
TOOLING:$  UNIT PRICE:$

## Rubber pressing mold
This is a standard rubber pressing mold used to make a cup sole style design. Simply put, this looks like a large waffle iron. This is made of steel.

You can see the mold has separate parts to mold bottom tread, side wall, and the top and inside of the cupsole. On this tooling you can see where the side wall and bottom parts of the tooling meet. This is called the parting line.

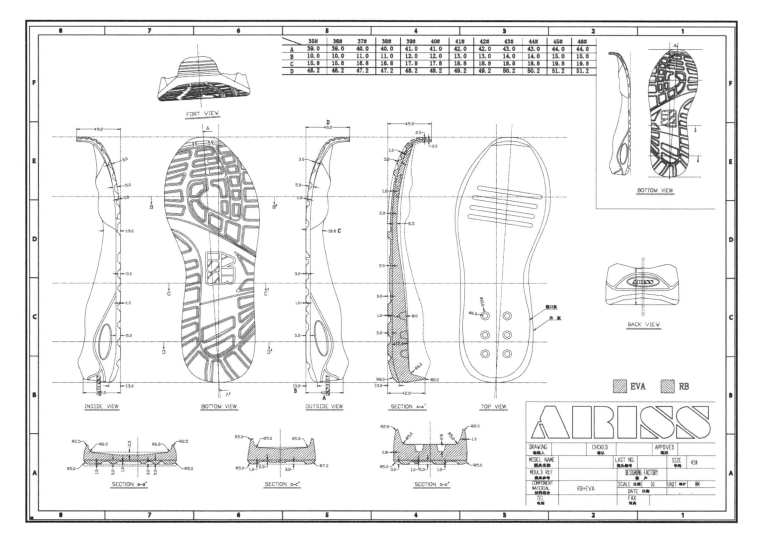

## Required blue print views

1. Medial side view
2. Bottom view
3. Lateral side view
4. Cross section down the length
5. Top view of the midsole
6. View of left side shoe (to confirm logos)
7. Toe view
8. Heel view
9. Cross section at critical points to see shoe detail
10. Texture notes or detailed cross sections
11. Material specs
12. Revision block to show who made drawing changes

This drawing will be sent by email, then corrected. A new model may require several rounds of revisions before the new design is made into a 3D CAD file.

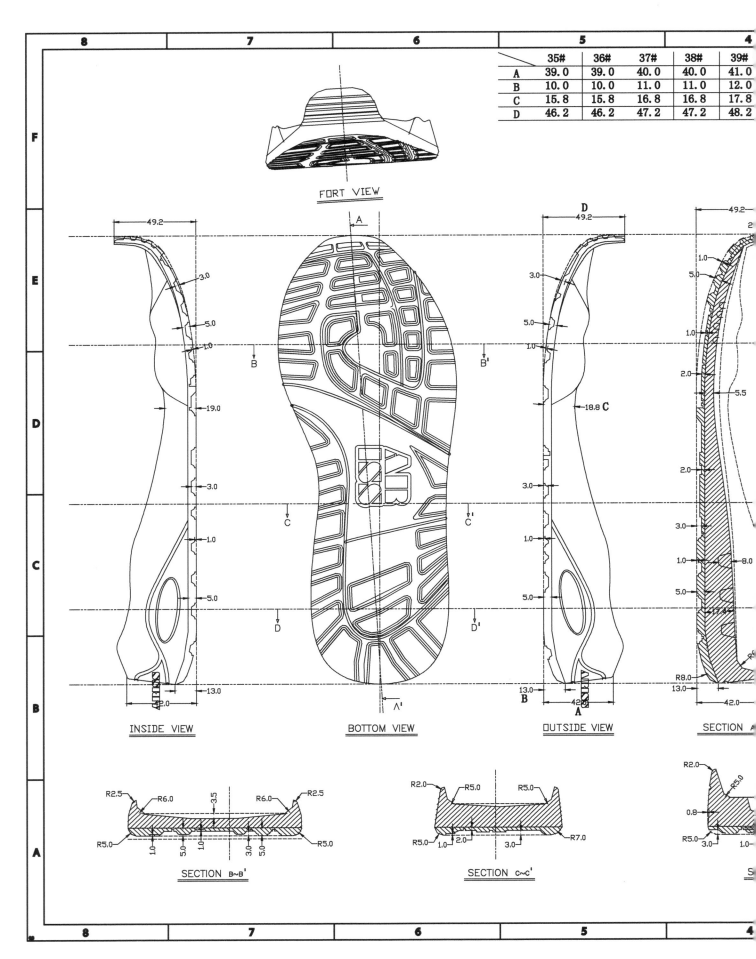

FORT VIEW

INSIDE VIEW

BOTTOM VIEW

OUTSIDE VIEW

SECTION A

SECTION B~B'

SECTION C~C'

53

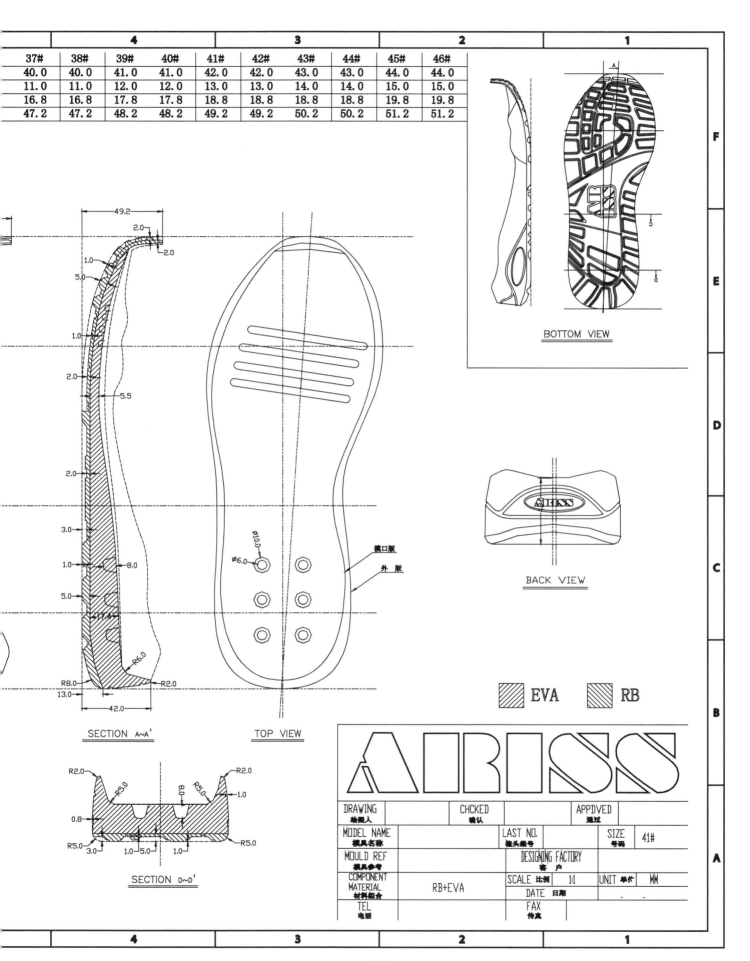

| | | 4 | | | | 3 | | | 2 | |
|---|---|---|---|---|---|---|---|---|---|---|
| 37# | 38# | 39# | 40# | 41# | 42# | 43# | 44# | 45# | 46# | |
| 40.0 | 40.0 | 41.0 | 41.0 | 42.0 | 42.0 | 43.0 | 43.0 | 44.0 | 44.0 | |
| 11.0 | 11.0 | 12.0 | 12.0 | 13.0 | 13.0 | 14.0 | 14.0 | 15.0 | 15.0 | |
| 16.8 | 16.8 | 17.8 | 17.8 | 18.8 | 18.8 | 18.8 | 18.8 | 19.8 | 19.8 | |
| 47.2 | 47.2 | 48.2 | 48.2 | 49.2 | 49.2 | 50.2 | 50.2 | 51.2 | 51.2 | |

BOTTOM VIEW

BACK VIEW

SECTION A~A'

TOP VIEW

SECTION D~D'

▨ EVA   ▨ RB

# AIRSS

| DRAWING 绘图人 | | CHCKED 确认 | | APPDVED 通过 | | | |
|---|---|---|---|---|---|---|---|
| MODEL NAME 模具名称 | | | LAST NO. 楦头编号 | | | SIZE 号码 | 41# |
| MOULD REF 模具参考 | | | DESIGNING FACTORY 客户 | | | | |
| COMPONENT MATERIAL 材料组合 | | RB+EVA | SCALE 比例 | | 1:1 | UNIT 单位 | MM |
| | | | DATE 日期 | | | | |
| TEL 电话 | | | FAX 传真 | | | | |

54

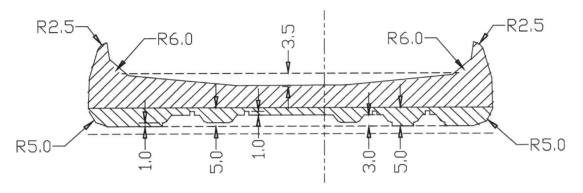

## SECTION  B~B'

Cross section views show the midsole and rubber thickness. Color dams are noted and the edge radius is called out.

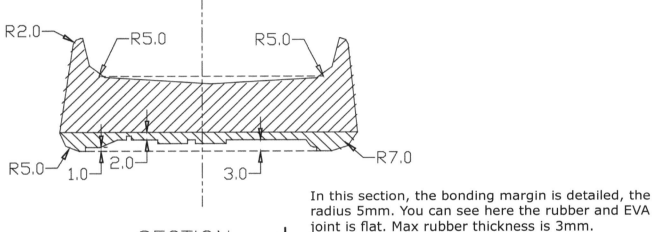

In this section, the bonding margin is detailed, the radius 5mm. You can see here the rubber and EVA joint is flat. Max rubber thickness is 3mm.

## SECTION  C~C'

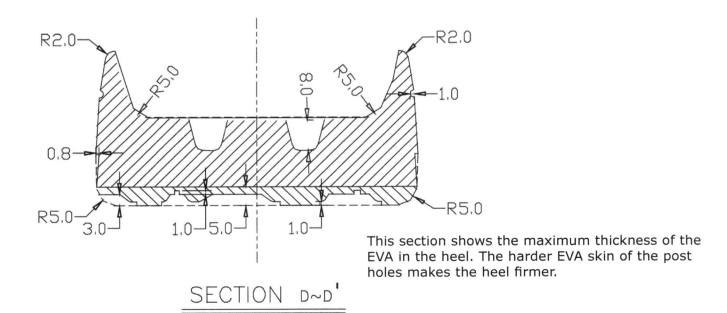

This section shows the maximum thickness of the EVA in the heel. The harder EVA skin of the post holes makes the heel firmer.

## SECTION  D~D'

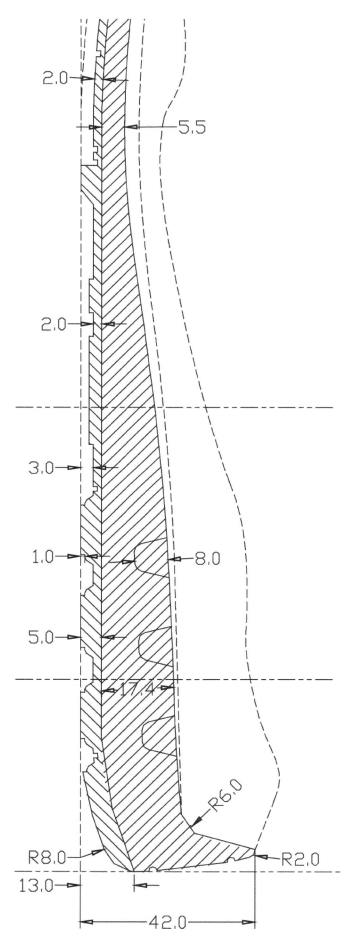

In this section, the bonding margin is detailed in the dotted line. For the connection of the upper the margin should be 8mm for a safe strong bond.

In this section, you can see the midsole heel lift over the length of the sole. This line should match the last bottom profile.

Here you can see the heel midsole height is 17.4mm, the fore foot is 5.5mm. You can also see the heel lift. It's 11.9mm.

## The 3D models woodcut

Once the 2D design blueprint for the outsole has been confirmed by the designers and developers, it's time for the mold factory to make the 3D CAD model. The 3D CAD model shows every aspect of the design. Every corner radius, color dam, and tread detail will be in the model. Once the 3D CAD model has been approved it's time to make a "woodcut" or "wooden mold."

This is when the tool comes to life in a 3D part you can touch. The woodcut is no longer made of wood, in today's shoemaking operations the model can be made by CNC cutting REN (Polyurethane Foam Blocks), 3D Printing, or SLA (Stereo-lithography).

With the woodcut in hand, the designers and developers can study the outsole design one last time before the metal tooling is cut. The wood model is often painted and presented in design meetings. The top net of the wood model can be machined to allow a lasted upper to sit down inside, this will let you see the complete shoe.

## Reviewing the woodcut

With the woodcut in hand, there are few things to check before you approve it. Any mistakes here will cost time and money so don't be afraid to mark-up the woodcut and send it back for revisions.

**1.** Are the color dams in the correct locations?

**2.** Are the logos oriented correctly?

**3.** Does the side wall have a tall enough bonding margin?

**4.** Make sure there are no tiny fins or strange intersections.

**5.** Check that the woodcut is cleanly cut, broken features are a signal that the design may have problems when cut in metal.

**6.** Bring it together with the lasted upper to confirm all design features line up.

**7.** Confirm the tread pattern is exactly what you want.

**8.** Review with the blueprint so you know exactly where the mold parting line is.

The "REN" or woodcut, will have every detail of the final metal mold. The designer must check every detail.

The mold maker will also be checking to make sure the metal tooling will be functional. For complicated molds the wood-cut is used in the metal casting process.

The tooling is made by metal casting or CNC machine work. Outsole molds are usually steel. EVA midsole molds can be made from cast aluminum. Heavy pinsensure the mold closes straight.

It requires many molds to make a production run of outsoles. Here, these molds are waiting at the pressing factory. While the shoe brands or shoe assembly factory may own the molds, they are often left at the rubber pressing factory. If a mold needs repairs or adjustments it will be sent back to the tooling shop. If you want your molds back you need to make sure the pressing factory is paid on time!

The deep groves are color dams. The dams control the flow of rubber inside the mold.

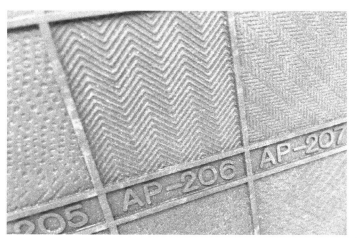

All the surfaces inside the mold require some type of texture. The most basic is simple "sandblast" specified in light, medium, or heavy.

The shoe designer has hundreds of different texture choices. Applied to the mold surface by acid etching process, any texture can be made by printing the design onto special release paper.

The texture supplier will have a huge book of rubber plates to pick from, or make your own design!

**CHAPTER 6**

# FOOTWEAR DEVELOPMENT PROCESS

While every shoe brand will have a slightly different development process, the basic procedure is the same. The process can be broken down into three main phases, each focusing on different aspects of development.

## Tech sample round
The goal is to create the pattern and outsole design.

## Photo sample round
The goal is to finalize color and material choices, creating shoes ready for catalog photography.

## Sales samples round
The goal is to make any final adjustments to pattern, color, and construction while producing samples for the salesmen.

The development process for a new shoe can take weeks, months, or years to complete depending on the design requirements. A new color for a shoe can be made in just a few weeks, while a new cushioning system may take years to engineer, develop, and test.

## Tech round development

The tech round is the first stage following the design cycle. This round will give the designer the first chance to see their shoe designs take shape in 3D form. The tech phase generally takes 6 to 8 weeks to create a new shoe from the design drawings.  This sounds like a long time, but keep in mind the typical R & D group may develop thirty new models at a time. The first phase is to produce one sample of each new shoe. A simple sneaker may have a prototype outsole mold or a borrowed sole unit from an existing shoe. This will give the developer a good idea of what the shoes will look like.

Over the course of the 6 to 8 weeks, the designers and developers will have a chance to see pattern trials, outsole blueprints, and material swatches. Both designers and developers may travel to the factory to review progress and speed up development. After many weeks, the samples may be hand carried or mailed to the designers by air freight.

This can be a fun time for the team. Like Christmas, the samples will arrive and be unpacked with great excitement! While some projects look great, others are failures. Typically, the design team will have a week to review the new samples, recommend changes, and prepare for the photo sample meeting.

With the new sneaker samples in hand, the product team will meet with sales and marketing teams to decide which new designs will go forward in development. The result of this phase will be a complete line of shoes ready to be photographed for the sales catalogs.

From the first phase, only 30% of the new items will go forward. Many items are changed, scrapped, or combined with others until only the best ideas go forward.

## Sample making

With the paper pattern finished, the design is passed to the sample cutters and stitchers to make the first test pattern.
The sample parts are carefully cut and stitched to create the first "pull over." The trial pattern is not the correct colors or materials. The assembled pattern is pulled over the shoe last.

## Pull overs

The pattern trial or "pull over" does not look like much to the untrained eye but the developers and designers can tell right away if there is more work to be done on the pattern.
With the test pattern in hand, the outsole drawings can be made to fit the lasted upper. The mold technicians will carefully measure the lasted upper to make sure the outsole parts fit correctly.

Now it's time to get the shoe bottom or "outsole" ready!

62

## Photo sample round

The photo sample round is another 6 to 8 weeks of work. The goal of this phase is to improve the new designs and make all the color and material choices. The designer and the product manager work together to merchandise the product line. Merchandising occurs when the new designs are arranged with the existing products to ensure a balanced mix of colors, materials, design themes, and price points.

For the photo sample round, the team may create 6 new colors to review and the best 3 or 4 will be selected.

Again, as with the tech phase, the photo sample patterns will be adjusted, outsole tooling opened, re-cut from scratch or repaired. The developers will often travel to the factory to check all the details. Usually, the developers will send the new collections to the factory then arrive 4 to 5 weeks later to review progress. This gives the shoe factory enough time to make pattern collections and find the correct color materials required to make the samples. The developers will review the raw materials and test patterns before giving the factory the green light to make the samples.

Photo samples are made only for review by the R & D team. Thus materials and logos may be painted or simulated without having to order hundreds of yards of custom dyed material. The developers may work at the factory to oversee the final assembly.

Only the best, most experienced stitchers, are selected to work in the sample room.

They must work quickly as the customer is always in a rush. Are the samples "handmade"? Yes, and so is the production!

## The final line build

With the photo samples now back in the design center, it is time to merchandise the final product line. Like a giant puzzle, the new shoes and old shoes are arranged on the wall. When the line selection is being worked on, there can be a hundred different shoes selected, and 200 more on the floor rejected or postponed. Once the line is arranged, the sales and marketing teams will have their say. Long hours, heated discussions, dented egos and wounded pride may result, but in the end, the line is settled.

The surviving shoes are quickly reviewed for any design changes, then organized for the photographer to get started. Once the line is set, it is time to order the salesmen's samples.

Depending on the size of the company's distribution network, anywhere from 10 pairs to a few hundred pairs of each new shoe will be ordered. Men's size 9 and women's size 7 are always ordered.

## The final development phase
## sales sample production

Depending on the number of samples to be produced, this phase will be approximately 9 to 10 weeks. Following the final line build, the developers will send off the final few changes for the shoe. Hopefully, the changes are small, and the factory can get started ordering materials. Unlike the photo samples that could be a mix of painted material and substitutions, the sales samples have to be the real deal. All color and materials must be correct.

Within a week of receiving the order, the factory will have ordered the materials. This is a key issue to follow up on as the lead time for some materials can be 4 to 5 weeks. While the factory is waiting for the new materials to arrive, the final pattern adjustments are reviewed and confirmed. The factory will also be making 1 set of metal cutting dies to make the sample size shoes. The mold factory will be finishing any modifications to the outsoles. This is also the first time the shoe will be made outside of the factory sample room. Some stitching problems are only discovered once the production stitching staff tries to mass produce the samples.

Just as with the photo sample round, the developers often visit the factory just in time to confirm the sales sample materials. The developer can also request for the sample room to make one more sample to review the details before the sales samples are produced. This is a critical time to review the progress, mistakes or delays can hurt a new shoes' chance of success.

## Will this shoe make it?

It has taken many months to get to this stage. Countless hours of design time, development time, and travel time for staff members traveling to factories around the world.

The catalogs have been printed. The salesmen have the sample shoes on the road, now it's time to see if the new design will make it to the public.

This can be a tense time for the design and marketing teams...waiting for the results from the salesmen. Do the shoe buyers love it or hate it? Is the price right? Do the samples look good or did they arrive dirty and wrinkled?

Good news! The new design made it. Now the shoe is passed to the production department. The production team will transform the sample into a real shoe!

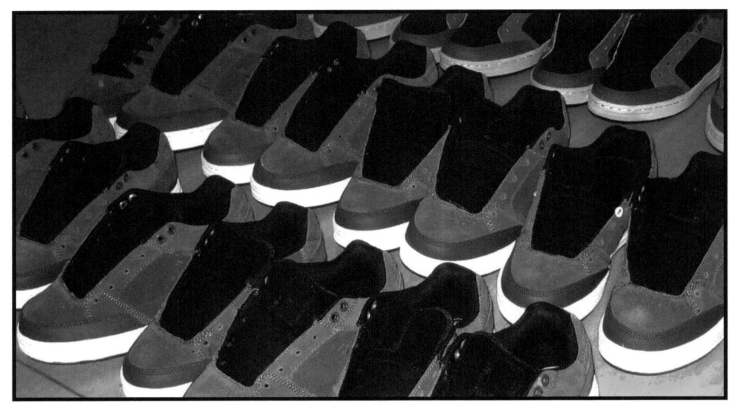

**CHAPTER 7**

# FOOTWEAR PRE-PRODUCTION

Once the new shoe design has been approved and orders have been placed, it is time to get serious about production. Pre-production or "commercialization" is a process that starts with a sample shoe and ends when every size has been fit tested and all the equipment for the entire size run is completed and approved.

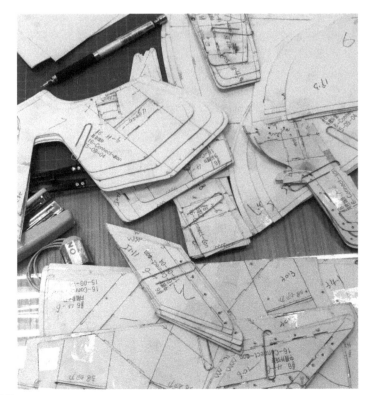

Paper patterns must be made for every size.

65

# Getting ready for production

Now that this shoe is going into the company's product line, the developer works with the factory staff to turn the nice looking samples into real functional shoes that can be efficiently produced. The sample shoe may look finished but it has not been prepared for a mass production.

A typical minimum production run is around 500 pairs. There is no maximum run. A popular shoe from a big brand could require millions of pairs.

The pre-production process starts with the "tear down" meeting. The tear down meeting is when the factory's production team takes over the project. The sales sample shoe, lasted upper, outsole parts, and paper patterns are collected together and the production team goes to work.

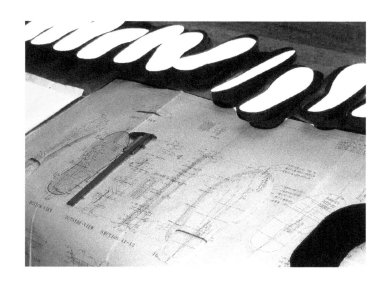

The production team is broken down into different departments. The managers from the material purchasing, rubber pressing, stitching, and assembly departments all review their portion of the project. The different departments look at every component and operation required to assemble the shoe.

The production engineers review the sequence of operations required to make the shoe. The factory staff is looking for details in the construction that could lead to quality problems, fitting issues, or difficult assembly processes that can cause delays.

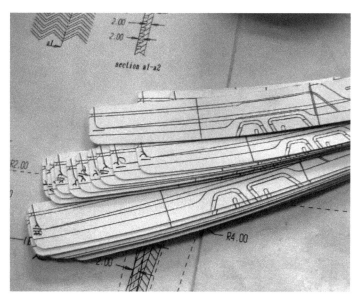

Once the sample size shoe has been approved and signed off, the development department goes to work "grading" the shoe. Grading is simply the creation of sizes. Sample development is only for size 9 for men and size 7 for women. Once the sample size shoe is confirmed all the other sizes can be made.

The size "grade" can include as many as 14 new sizes. This work is done by machine. The computer is programed with the dimensions of the lasts. It makes the test patterns. The test patterns are then corrected by human effort.

The factory must then make the patterns, cutting dies, and outsole tooling for every size. This can take 60 days. Once the equipment is ready, test shoes, one of each size, must be made and checked. Once every size is confirmed the factory is ready to start production.

## Ready for production

With the upper patterns graded to cover all the sizes, it's time to make the cutting dies.

The cutting dies are exactly like big cookie cutters, except these cutting dies have sharpened steel edges. A production run of shoes will require dozens, if not hundreds, of different cutting dies. Every shoe part needs its own die. Left and right sides vary in every size.

On this cutting die, you can see the size marks that are nipped into the edge. This code tells the worker what size the parts are.

Outsole tooling must be made for every size.

A size run of cutting dies in storage waiting for production.

67

LEGION 中底饰片 5-6#
LEGION 中底饰片 7-8#
9-10
LEGION 中底饰片
LEGION 中底饰片 11-12#
13-14
14

## CHAPTER 8

# SHOE MATERIAL PREPARATION

Material preparation is the most difficult and time-consuming part of making a modern shoe.

Before a single stitch can be made, all the upper parts, bottom units, and packing materials have to be ready. Components for our sneaker come from many different factories and even other countries. Entire departments inside the factory are dedicated to purchasing, processing, and inspecting the raw materials that go into the sneaker.

A factory store house can be a great place to find materials for samples if you are designing on the fly.

A neatly organized material store house.

## Materials

You can see from the sample specification that even the most basic sneaker has dozens of components. It takes a large team of raw material buyers in the factory to keep these components flowing to the sample rooms and production lines.

When you consider a large factory may have many customers, each with several seasons of shoes simultaneously in production and in development, the number of unique materials is easily into the thousands.

The material buyers are responsible for forecasting the amount required, negotiating the purchase price, and calculating the lead time. The buyer must have the right amount of material at the factory in time for production.

Once inside the factory, each component must be checked for quality, color, and quantity. After the material is approved, each part is cut, and logos are printed or embroidered. Only after every part is ready, (even a simple shoe may have 50 parts) can stitching begin.

Everything needed for the shoe is in the store house, including the cardboard boxes, tissue, hang tags, etc.

This is a typical cutting department. A cutter is paired with a worker that stacks and sorts the parts.

This is a hydraulic safety press in the cutting room. Both green buttons must be pressed.

Under the material is a plastic cutting mat. This keeps the material edges clean, but must be replaced regularly. The cutter carefully places the die on the leather. The parts are close together to reduce "cutting waste".

Cutting dies are grouped together to make efficient cutting. The parts for one shoe may be cut by several workers.

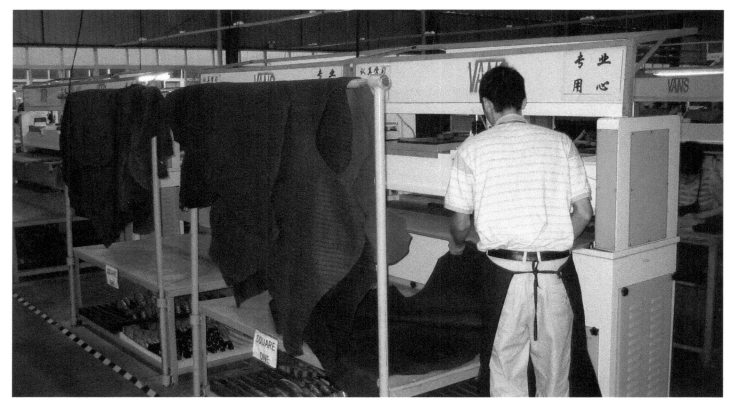

Leather hide must be hung to insure the leather will not wrinkle after cutting.

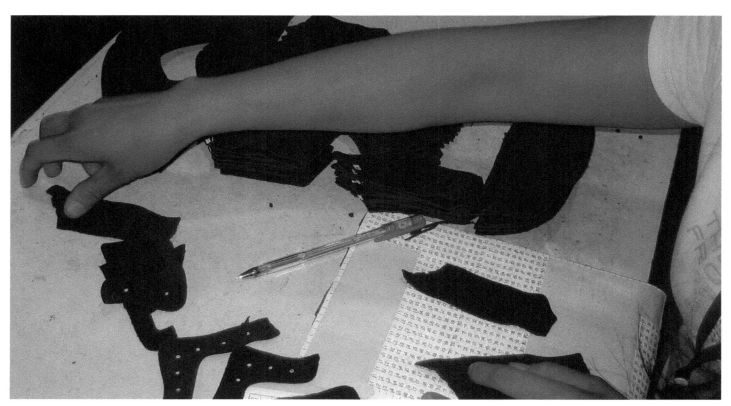

Sitting behind the cutter, another worker sorts the parts, making sure the colors match. The stickers are used to group the parts together. Like a shoe making kit.

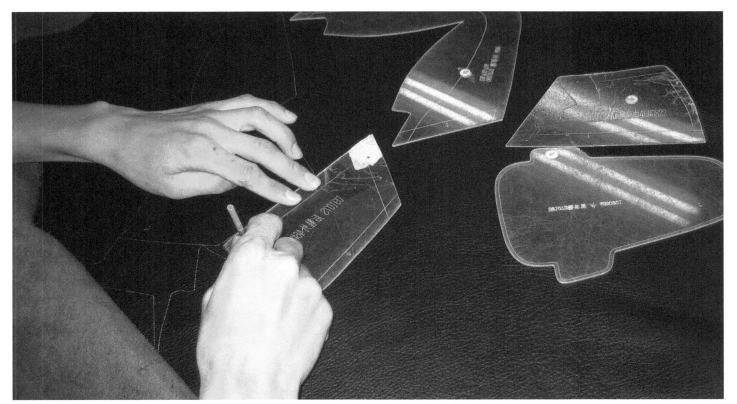

Full grain leather can be expensive, $8.00 to $15.00 a foot. This leather is marked by experienced cutters.

Soft lining leathers must be marked and cut by hand.

## Material processing

Once all the parts are cut, it is time to make them into shoe components. The parts need to be marked with assembly guide lines, edges skived, and logos printed or welded. The parts must then be organized into kits so they stay together.

A good printing room will have lots of ventilation. Spray cement holds the parts in place. A drying machine speeds up the process. The little knobs are used to align the screens at every station.

This is actually one embroidery machine! 20 stitching heads all moving together.
This complicated machine is kept in its own room to be free of dust and to block its noise.

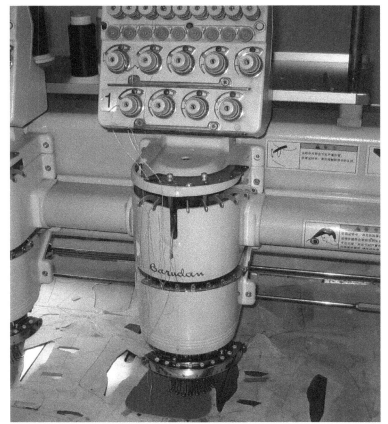

This is a 9 color machine.

**CHAPTER 9**

# UPPER STITCHING OPERATIONS

All the parts are cut and marked and it is time for the stitching lines to assemble the upper.

The stitching department is the heart of the shoe factory. Stitching is the most complicated and labor intensive part of shoe construction. Depending on the complication of the sneaker design it may take 800 to 1000 stitchers to support one assembly line.

Yes, every shoe is made by hand!

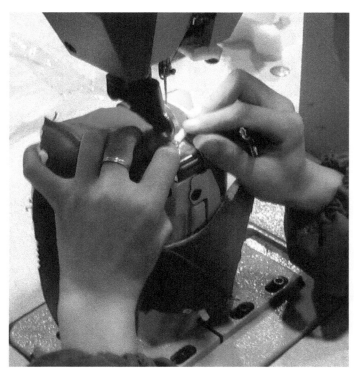

## Stitching

The accuracy and organization of the stitching department largely determines the quality of the finished shoe. The stitching operations of the sneaker construction are broken down into many smaller procedures. Each procedure is handled by a different sewing machine operator.

This is key to ensuring the quality of the sneaker. Each stitching operation is linked to a specific stitcher, if a problem is discovered it is easily tracked and corrected.

Also, because the same stitcher repeats the same operation for hundreds or even thousands of pairs, the task is soon mastered. Let's have a look at the stitching operations up close.

A busy stitching department.

Here, the upper is closed and the lining is attached. In this case, the upper is turned out to avoid getting glue on the lining while the rubber heel counter is being cemented into the shoe.

Here, the tongue lining is attached to the tongue facing. The other worker is stuffing the tongue foam and is making sure the seam is completely turned out.

# Stitching order of operations

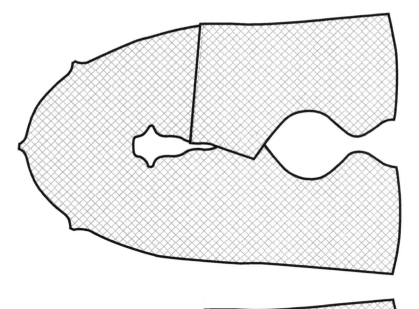

The first operation is to join the shoe lining parts together. For this lightweight training shoe, the lining and upper mesh are the same component. Air mesh or mesh combined with foam and lining. All the upper parts can now be attached. This base layer can be a non-woven fabric or fabric reinforcing layer.

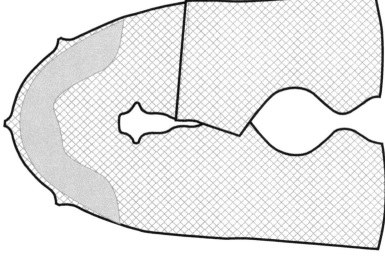

With the lining complete, the toe puff is attached. This part usually has a heat fusible backing, so stitching is not required to hold it in place. For the vamp area, the fewer stitches the better to ensure comfort.

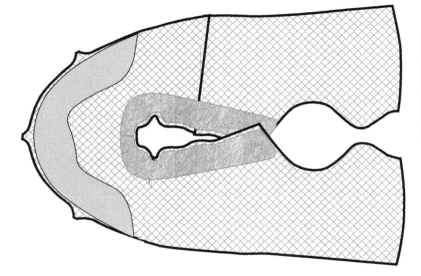

Next, the eyestay reinforcements are attached. This material is called "super tough." It can be attached by stitching or by self-adhesive backing. Used to reinforce punched holes and metal eyelets, super tough ensures the shoe laces cannot rip or stretch the upper.

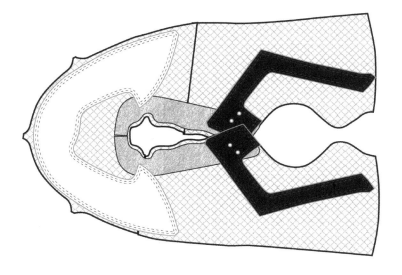

Here the toe tip/mudguard part is sewn down to the vamp. This covers the toe reinforcement. This part is laid under the eyestay so it must be sewn on first.

The collar underlay is also attached.

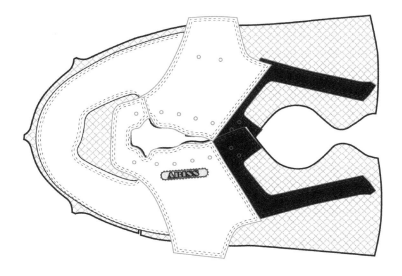

Now the two eyestay parts are sewn to each other, then attached to the upper. The eyestay parts cover and trap the reinforcements. While the pattern parts have the lace holes already punched, these will need to be punched again after the lining and reinforcement layers are assembled.

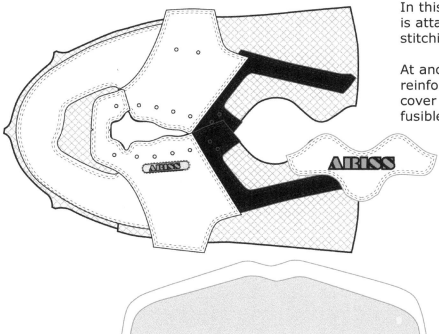

In this operation, the heel panel, or mustache is attached. The logos are applied before any stitching operations.

At another workstation, the heel reinforcement is attached to the counter cover part. The reinforcement is attached by fusible backing or by glue.

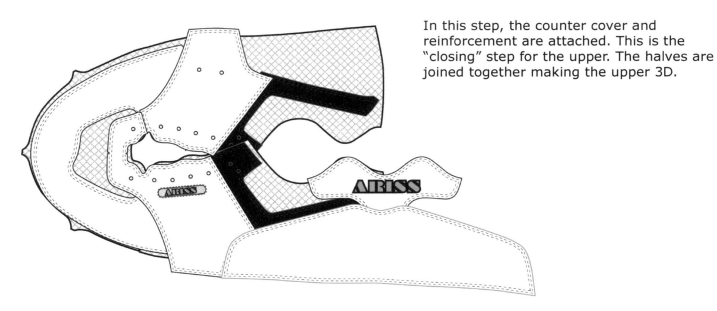

In this step, the counter cover and reinforcement are attached. This is the "closing" step for the upper. The halves are joined together making the upper 3D.

The heel counter is assembled into the shoe but has not been fully shaped.

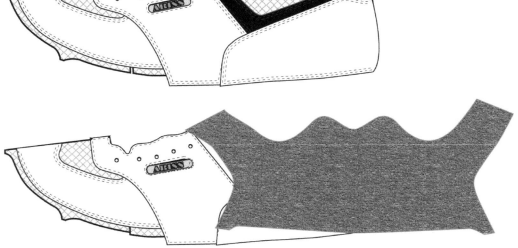

With the upper closed, the lining parts can be attached. The lining fabric is usually laminated to a 4mm PU foam layer. This gives the lining some extra softness and allows the fabric to be handled. The lining is attached to the outside facing so it can be turned into the shoe.

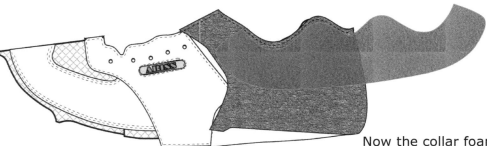

Now the collar foam is attached. The foam will be coated with PU glue or sprayed with hot melt adhesive. With the foam collar bonded in, the lining can be folded back into place.

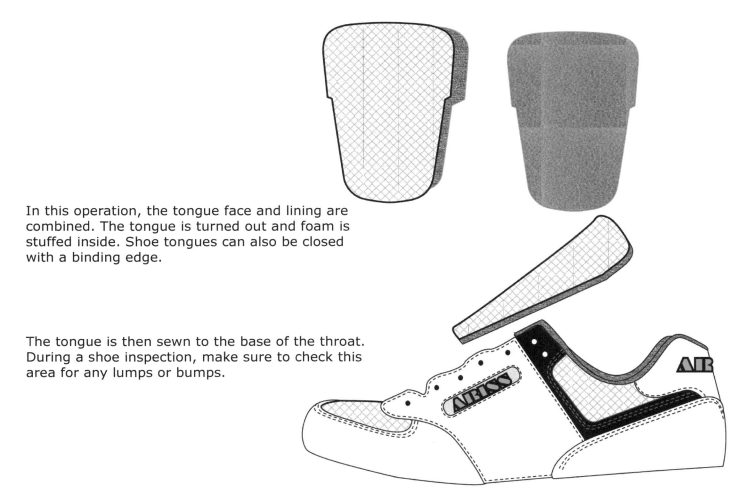

In this operation, the tongue face and lining are combined. The tongue is turned out and foam is stuffed inside. Shoe tongues can also be closed with a binding edge.

The tongue is then sewn to the base of the throat. During a shoe inspection, make sure to check this area for any lumps or bumps.

With the tongue installed and lining in place the upper may have some final forming operations. The toe area is placed in a small heater to soften the plastic toe puff. This is made from a thermo-forming plastic usually Surlyn. The upper is then clamped into a toe cooling fixture that sets the shape. The same operation is then done to the heel counter of the shoe.

The upper is completed with the attachment of the bottom strobel sock. This upper is now ready for final assembly on the lasting line.

## CHAPTER 10

# OUTSOLE RUBBER PRESSING

We can thank Charles Goodyear for his perseverance. In 1844, after years of experimentation, he invented the process of heating natural rubber mixed with sulfur. He called it vulcanization, and it is still how we make rubber today. With the right combination of mixing, heat, and curing agents, sticky natural rubber is transformed into tough and colorful sneaker bottoms.

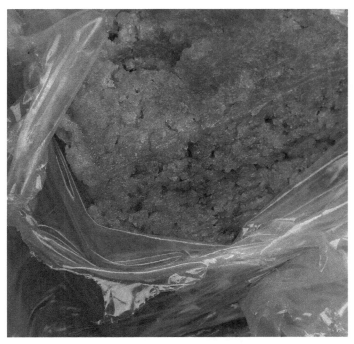

The natural rubber is partially cured for easy storage transport.

# Rubber pressing

The rubber pressing operations are usually sub-contracted to a factory that specializes in the compounding and pressing of the rubber parts. The rubber mixing operations are messy and pressing rooms are uncomfortably hot, so these are best done outside of the actual shoe factory.

Also, the rubber pressing factory will have many customers allowing the presses to run higher volume efficiently.

The rubber pressing operation begins with the mixing of the rubber components. Depending on the performance requirements of the rubber outsole, natural and synthetic rubbers are combined with the curing agents of sulfur or peroxide.

The rubber compound controls the following attributes:
Hardness  (Shore "A" scale)
Slip Resistance
Durability (NBS Rating)
Specific Gravity (weight)
Chemical Resistance
Heat Resistance
Tensile Strength
Tear Resistance

The basic skate shoe is rubber and is specified as follows:
NSB 400 Shore A 65  + or - 3  SG 1 to 1.2

Once the rubber recipe is selected and tested, the production rubber can be mixed, formed and pressed.

Natural rubber from Thailand or Indonesia. ISNR 20 (TSR 20) is general purpose rubber.

The blocks of uncured synthetic and natural rubber are measured out, ready to be mixed.

Batches of synthetic rubber and additives wait to be mixed.

90

Once the rubber has been completely mixed, it is run off the mill in long sheets. The rubber is very much like taffy at this point. The uncured rubber can be ripped by hand or cleanly cut into shapes.

The rubber is now cut into shapes to make the color blocks for the outsole. With the rubber mixed and parts cut to fit the design, the outsole can be pressed.

The rubber outsole pressing is done in a mold that looks like a large waffle mold. The top and bottom of the mold are made from cast or machined steel and joined with a strong hinge allowing the mold to be opened and closed.

Dry components are mixed together.

After the dry components are mixed together, they are moved to a rolling mill.

Out of the water and into a power bath to stop the rubber from sticking to itself.

A worker loads the rubber onto a storage rack.

Here, the sheets are set aside waiting to be cut.

Raw materials and mixed rubber in storage waiting to be cut.

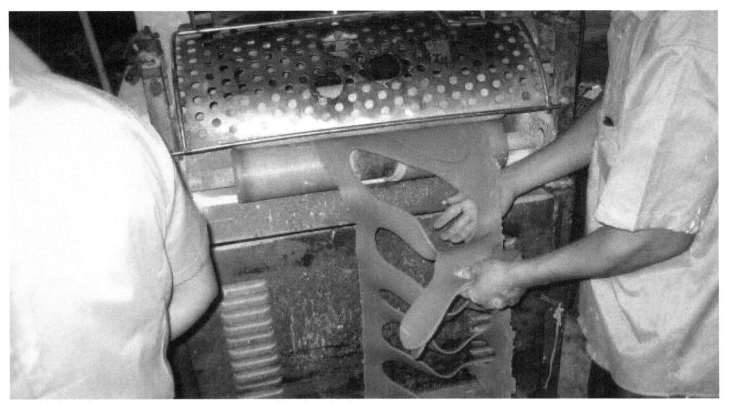

For high volume parts, an automatic cutter is used.

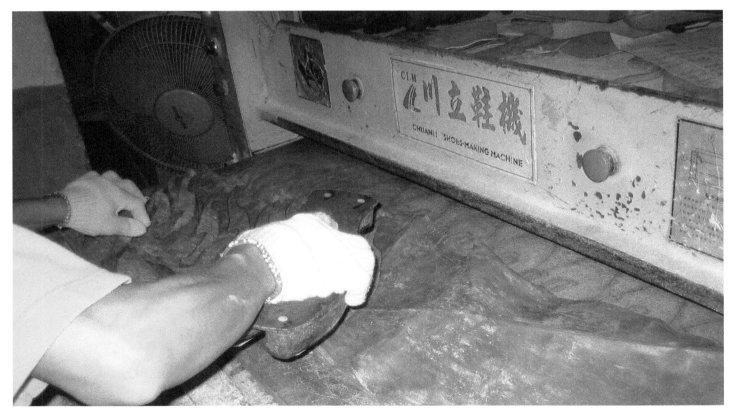

Uncured rubber is very sticky so it has been powdered for easy cutting.

Here the coloring agents are being mixed in.

In just a few minutes the mixing is done.

Uncured color samples waiting to be checked.

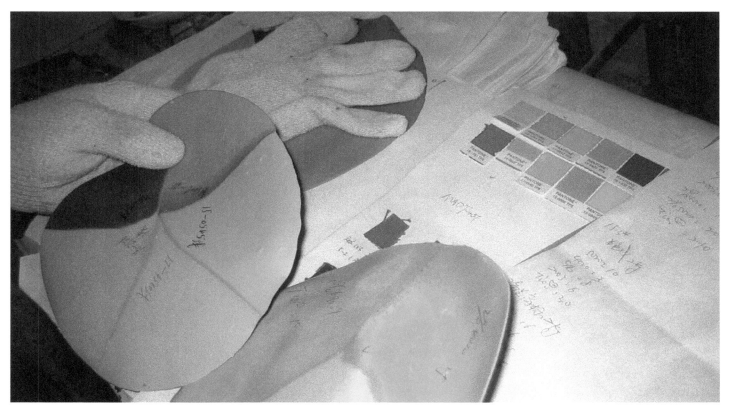

Here, a worker is checking the cured rubber against the pantone color chips and the confirmed rubber samples.

Every shoe size needs its own mold. A standard size run will be 14 molds. A mold can cost $2000 per size. A complete set can cost $30,000 to $100,000 USD. For big orders you will need extras of the "gut" sizes like 9,10,11.

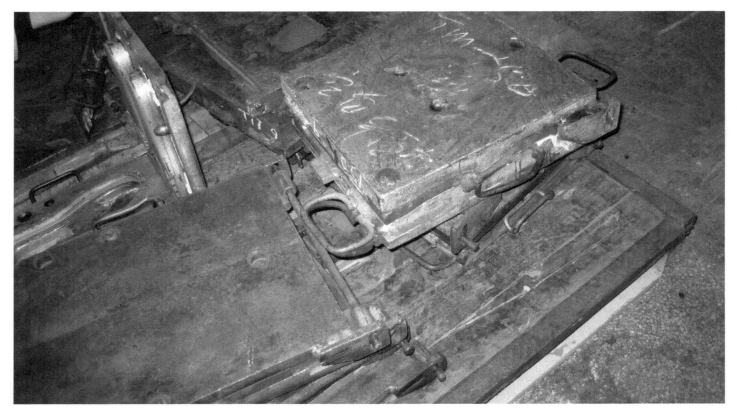

The outsole mold is like a big hinged waffle iron made of cast or machined steel or aluminum. Handles allow the mold to be pulled from the press.

A large rubber pressing room with many banks of presses. Note the high ceiling to let the heat escape. Each operator handles several press openings at once. The uncured rubber is stacked on top, pressed parts below.

The deep groves inside the mold allow you to make an "egg crate" pattern. This is lighter than a solid block of rubber.

This is the bottom side of the mold with the tread pattern.

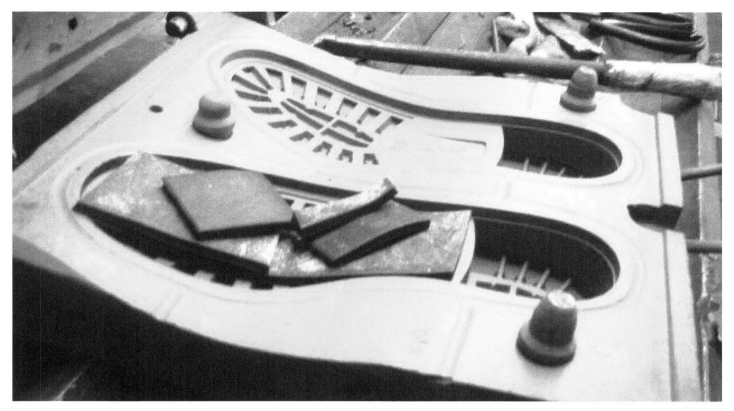

This mold is stuffed with raw rubber. When this mold is closed the rubber will fill the cavities.

The rubber will flow inside the mold. You can also see how the rubber "flashes out" around the edges. A properly designed and correctly filled mold will have a thin layer of flash.

The mold is open, the heel logos are in the mold now. Here you can see the waffle in the top mold.

Here is the raw rubber waiting to be loaded into the mold.

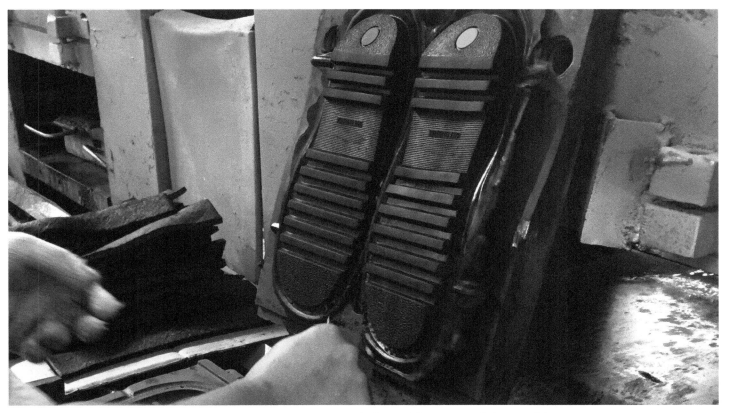

The mold is open, the rubber is cooling. Time to peel the rubber out of the mold.

The rubber is cool now and can be handled. The extra rubber flashing out from the edge ensures the mold is totally full of rubber. Now we are ready for trimming.

The uncured parts are ready for loading into the mold.

The soft rubber is being pressed into a shallow heel logo.

The logo is two colors, grey and white. You can see the tiny letters are made this way.

Now, the bottom tread rubber is added on top of the heel logo.

The side wall plate has been lifted off the base with a pry bar. Time to push the hot parts out.

This looks like trash, but all it needs is a little trimming and touch up.

The finished parts cooling. The flash ensures the mold was totally filled. You can see this outsole does not have egg crate inside. This empty space will be filled with die cut EVA sheeting to provide cushioning. The curved edge on the inside is to create a large bonding margin for the upper to rest on. The holes are molded to save some weight. The size mark is molded to make sure the parts are not mixed up.

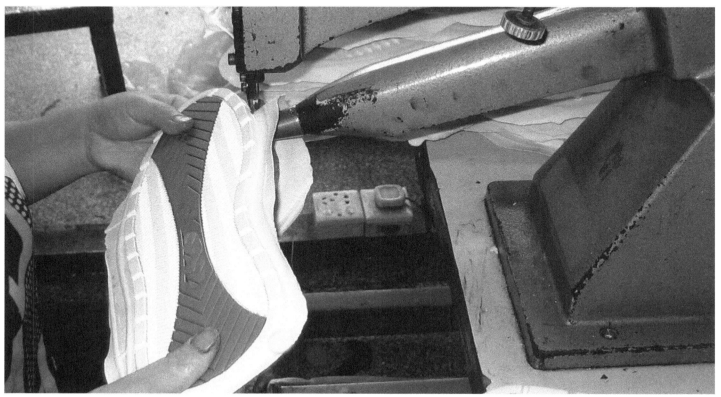

An electric driven edge trimmer makes short work of all the flash. The very sharp blade cuts very close. You can barely see the mold parting lines.

## CHAPTER 11

# EVA MIDSOLE FORMING

EVA or Ethylene Vinyl Acetate foam is what gives the modern shoe its spring! EVA is the most common foam used in athletic shoes. Your shoes would be heavy and painful without it. It's lightweight, easy to form into complex shapes, and can be made in almost any color.

## How is EVA made?

The modern athletic shoe will almost always have some cushioning foam inside. We call this the midsole. For a running shoe, 15mm of molded foam is standard. Other types of shoes like baseball cleats or track racing shoes may have just 5mm or even less. EVA foam is by far the most common foam used for midsoles.

It's light, waterproof, durable, and resists permanent compression. A properly made running shoe midsole can last 500 miles or more!

Before we discuss how EVA foam is made, let's talk about what foam really is. Foam is a flexible plastic with millions of tiny air bubbles trapped inside. In this case, our plastic is ethylene vinyl acetate. Depending on the individual foams' formulation and density, EVA can be mushy, soft and bendable, or rock hard.

We are going to look at the two types of EVA forming: cold pressing sheet foam, and hot pressing preforms. Both are very common and you will often find a shoe with a hot pressed midsole and cold pressed footbed, or a shoe with a die-cut sheet for the midsole and footbeds.

The dry raw materials are imported from Japan, Korea, the United States, and Germany. The formula includes the plastic resins, some fillers, coloring, and the blowing agent.

The blowing agent is a chemical combination that creates tiny gas bubbles in the plastic material when heated.

With the expansion press closed, the heat and pressure are cranked up. The pipes running to the press are full of hot oil. Inside the press, the raw EVA enters a critical state and the blowing agent creates the tiny air bubbles making the foam.

From the mixer, the raw EVA is mill rolled into thin "calendar" sheets just like rubber compound.

Out of the expansion press, the raw EVA mixture is now a huge sheet of foam.

The raw pellets are placed into an expansion mold to make preforms for hot EVA compression molding. Just a few years ago the factories used die cut sheets to hand make the preforms.

These are the expanded preforms ready for the final molding operations.

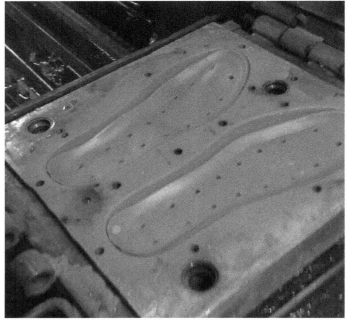

The preform is pushed into the final mold. This mold is very hot and will cause the foam skin to remelt and will reactivate the blowing agent (re-foaming). This is called hot pressing EVA.

Hot pressed parts have a strong skin, higher density and fine details. Almost all running shoes are made this way.

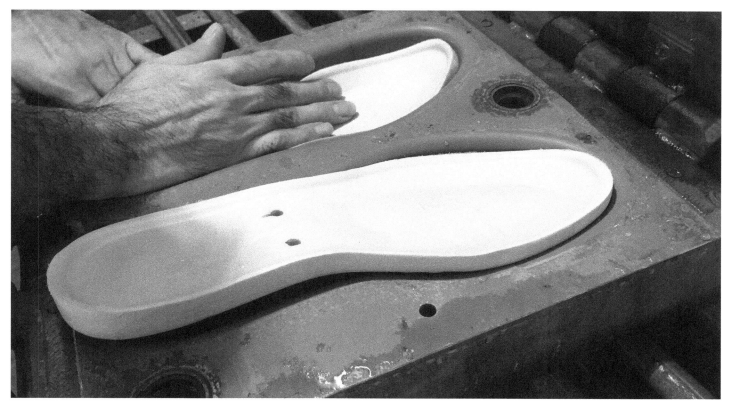

Here the worker is loading the preform into the mold. The preform is tight, then the heat and pressure cause the foam to re-expand filling the mold cavity so the parts take all the details from the mold surface.

Here the preforms are stacked with the finished parts in the molding factory.

# CHAPTER 12

# THE SHOE ASSEMBLY LINE

After months of work, grading designs, testing patterns, building tooling, and collecting materials from around the world, the shoes can finally be made. The stitched uppers are pulled from the storehouse, and the outsoles have been delivered from the rubber factory, final assembly is where it all comes together.

## Two construction types
There are two main methods of sneaker assembly: the modern cold cement, and classic vulcanized. The vulcanized shoe construction is a much older technology, and its usage has dropped in favor of the modern cold cement construction.

## Cold Cement Construction

Cold cement construction allows the use of modern lightweight plastic, foam, and mesh materials due to the lower temperatures required for bonding. Every modern high-performance athletic shoe for running, basketball, etc. is made by the cold cement process.

The typical cold cement running shoe with a mesh tongue, synthetic leather accents, and EVA midsole with rubber outsole.

## Vulcanized Shoe Construction

The vulcanized shoe construction process is the classic way to make a sneaker. Due to the high temperature required to vulcanize or cook the rubber outsole, the material options are limited. Canvas and suede leather are common.

The typical vulcanized sneaker with a simple cotton canvas upper and tongue. The upper is very thin with minimal tongue and collar lining. All the upper materials are heat resistant.

# Cold cement construction

In the cold cement process, the shoe upper is prepared with the strobel bottom connected to it. The strobel bottom or "sock" closes the upper, and it's now prepared to have the last slipped inside. The last can be plastic or metal.

The strobel material is a very tough fabric with low stretch and is marked with straight lines to help show if the upper is twisted or rotated on the last.

The upper is then steamed to soften the materials and the last is inserted. Once the last is inside the upper and temporary shoelaces pulled tight, the upper is cooled to shrink the upper tight to the last.

The shoe may have a plastic or fabric part installed on top of the tongue to protect the surface from damage and drift during the lasting operations. Several machines can be used to make sure the upper is pulled tight. A toe lasting machine and heel lasting machine also help to ensure the upper is pulled tight, this permanently sets the upper shape to the last.

While the upper is being lasted, the sole unit is being prepared. In this case, a rubber cup sole is made with the EVA foam cushioning component cemented inside. This is done in a separate process that's called stock fitting.

The upper is marked for cement application. Now that the upper is lasted tightly and the outside unit is complete, the two pieces come together. The rubber sole unit will receive a coating of primer and cement.

The outsole will get its own special primer designed for EVA and rubber. The shoe upper is also prepared with its own special primer and cement. After the contact cement and primer has been completely dried in the heating tunnels, the two pieces are joined together by hand.

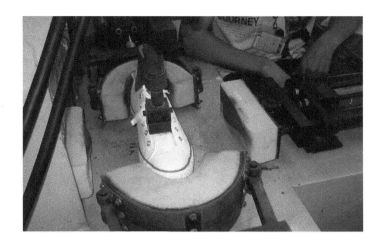

Once the shoe is pressed together, it is often put in the cooling tunnel to set the glue. After the cooling tunnel, a shoe de-lasting machine is used to push the last out of the shoe without wrinkling the upper.

The sneaker is complete at this point and the worker can insert the footbed and attach the final laces. The new sneaker is ready for inspection, cleaning, and packing.

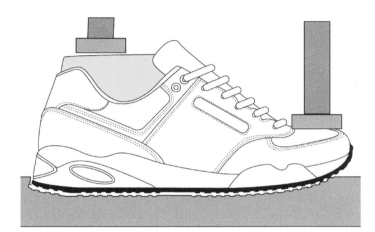

# Vulcanized construction

The difference between vulcanized and cold cement construction is in the method for attaching the outsole. Cold cement requires the outsole unit to be complete when attached to the upper, while the vulcanized outsole parts are attached to the upper piece by piece.

In the vulcanized process, the uncured rubber foxing tape must be made just before assembly. If the rubber parts age, they will not bond correctly to the other shoe parts. When attaching the foxing tape, we will need the bottom tread component of the shoe. This part has already been molded, it's about 90% vulcanized, so it's still a little bit soft and can be bonded in the assembly process. The bottom will also have the midsole filler added. The filler material is gray rubber with some air bubbles blown inside, it's made from the recycled uncured foxing tape. For vulcanized construction, you cannot use EVA foam as the high heat of the vulcanizing process will destroy the foam.

For vulcanized construction, the last must be made of aluminum to survive the oven temperature. The metal last heats up and cools down quickly.

The first step in the assembly process is to lightly cement the lasting board to the bottom of the last, just enough to hold it in place during the lasting operation. The lasting board is a paper fiberboard that provides stiffness to the finished shoe.

Lasting boards are made of different materials and can be stiff or flexible, thin or thick. Next, the last and upper are taken to the lasting machine. The toe lasting machine pulls the upper down onto the last and securely bonds the two parts together in one operation. Once the shoe heel and waist of the shoe are lasted, the upper is ready for the outsole.

The first step of the vulcanized outsole assembly process is similar to the cold cement process. The upper and the rubber sole parts all received their coating of primer and cement. Now, the rubber bottoms with the cushioning wedge are bonded together with the upper.

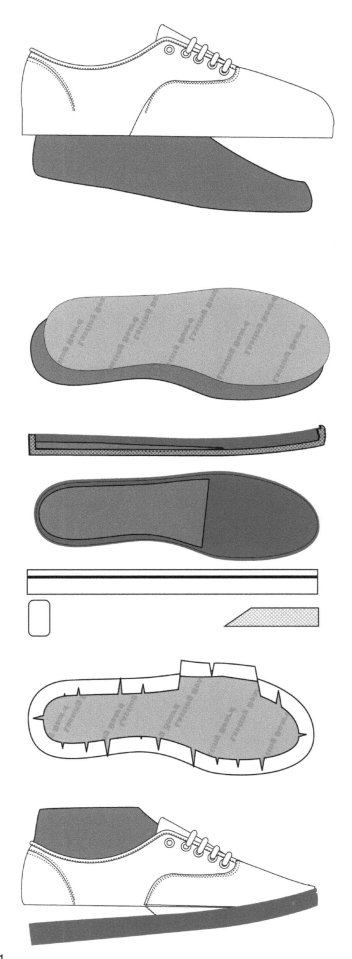

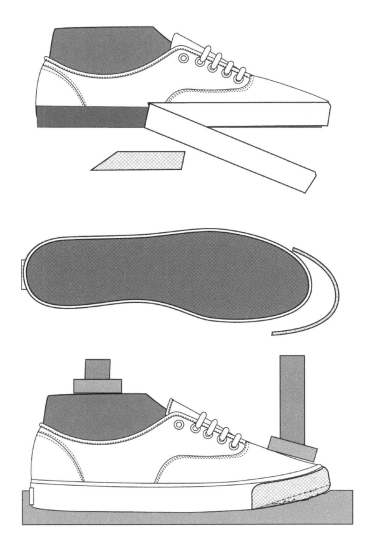

After sole pressing, the foxing tape, made of the uncured rubber, is carefully wrapped around the shoe. The foxing tape covers the rubber outsole part and overlaps up onto the upper. The foxing tape must cover 5mm of the upper to have a solid bond. The shoe can now have the extra toe tape added; then a rear logo will be applied to cover the joining seam.

With the tape applied, it's time to trim off any extra rubber with a hot knife and make sure there are no gaps. With the last still inside the shoe, it is placed on a steel rack so it can be wheeled into the oven.

The shoe will be in the vulcanizing oven for several hours. It is heated so the uncured foxing tape and the sole unit will fuse together.

After cooling, the last is removed, the footbed inserted, and laces added. The shoe is ready for final inspection, cleaning, and packing.

The uncured rubber is loaded into the mill for mixing.

The uncured rubber is fed into an extrusion mill to make a thick strip.

The black stripes are extruded and pulled by the traction roller.

The tension stretches the stripes into fine black pin lines.

Here the black pin lines are rolled together with the white base tape. When the tape is cured these will be fused together. You can see the large roller has a texture pattern on its surface.

The rubber tape is then cooled in a water bath.

After the water bath, the tape is dried, powder coated, then cut to length.

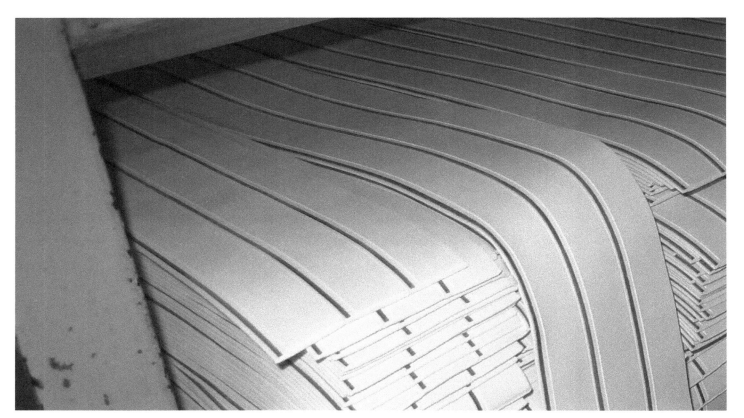

The finished foxing tape is now ready for the assembly line. This tape must be used within a few days.

This is the extrusion head. This bolts onto the mill to create different patterns of tape. This one has 3 colors.

The factory has a huge library of different tape extrusion heads.

The orange rubber is fed into the extrusion machine to make a color stripe.

This is a two color extrusion mill. The white and black rubber are fed into the mill and combined.

Into the cooling water bath.

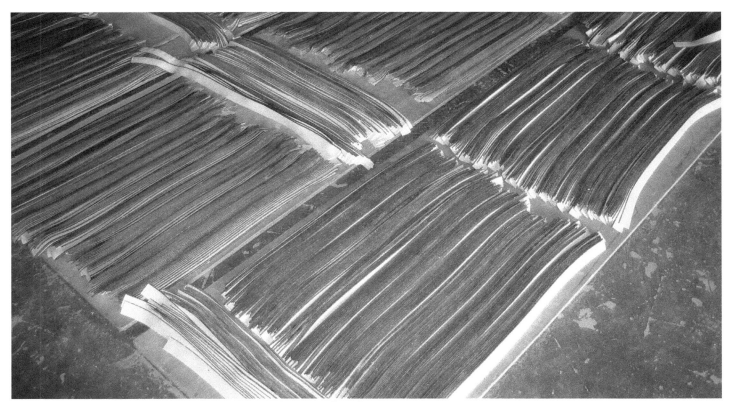

A big production run will require many thousands of tape sections.

Old tape cannot be used, after a few days it will lose its ability to stick and fuse properly. This pile of tape will be re-milled and used to make bonding filler or cushioning filler.

The worker is trimming raw rubber to make the heel logo or "license plate."

This is a tiny version of the rubber press, just for logos.

The knives are kept hot!

A worker uses a hot knife to cut outsoles. Note the metal pattern.

Here, the toe tips are cut and stacked, waiting for assembly. The raw rubber can only sit for a few days before it must be recycled.

The toe tip is glued before the rubber is applied. The thin sheet of rubber has been coated in glue before it is applied and pulled tight.

The uncured rubber is soft and takes the shape.

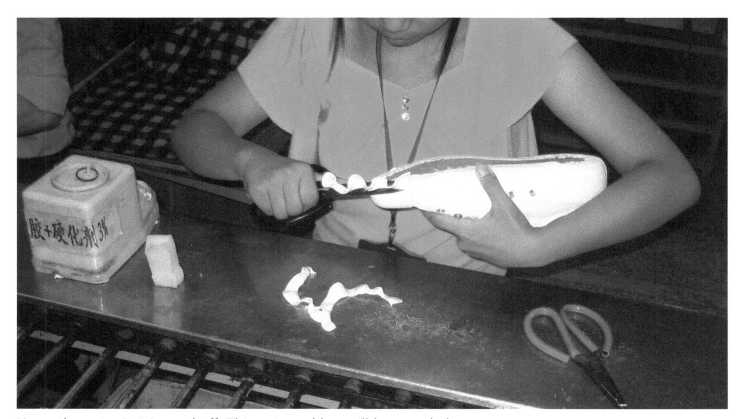

Here, the extra is trimmed off. This extra rubber will be recycled.

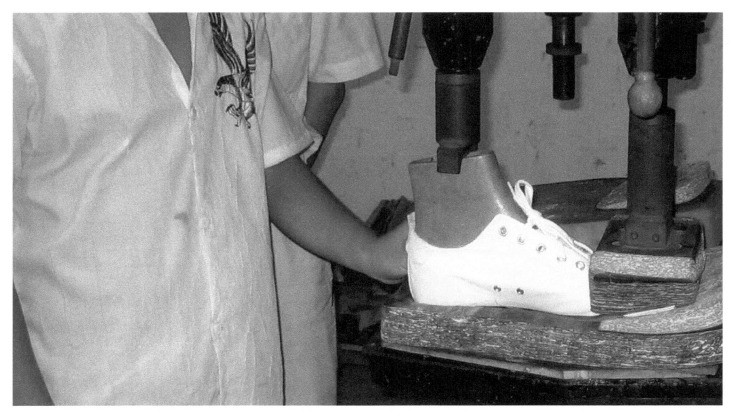

The toe tip and outsole bottom are pressed by machine before the foxing tape is applied.

The tape is ready for processing. You can see this tape has a printed design to match with the upper.

Cement is applied to both the upper and the foxing tape.

The foxing tape is wrapped.

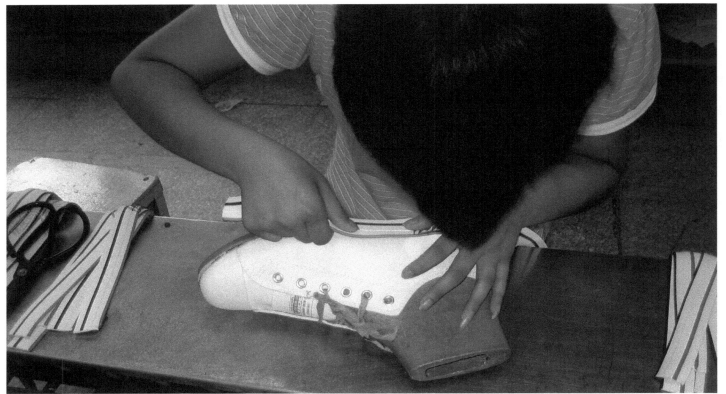

Carefully, the worker aligns the foxing logo to the logo printed on the upper.

Next, the toe foxing is applied to cover the seams. You can see the rubber edge on the bottom still needs to be trimmed.

The side foxing is pressed.

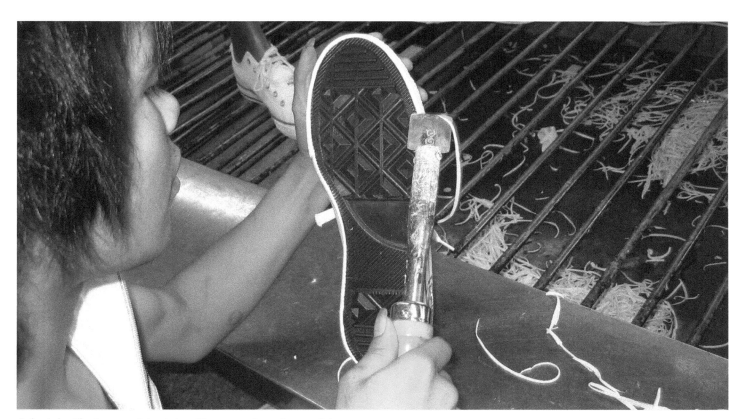

A hot knife is used to trim the overlapping rubber.

Once the shoes are assembled and trimmed, they are loaded onto metal carts. The lasts are still inside to hold the shape. The shoes are steam heated for several hours to cure the rubber.

Out of the oven, now they are ready for foam footbeds and laces.
The worker glues a small latex foam wedge to the footbed.

# THE SHOE LAST

The shoe last is the starting point of every shoe design. The last is a foot-shaped form made of molded plastic, carved wood, or cast aluminum. Used in both the development and production of shoes, the last sets the size, silhouette, and outline of the shoe. The last is critical to the shape of a shoe.

The shape of the last determines the fit, performance, ergonomics, and styling of a shoe. It is also what makes a shoe suitable for playing basketball, climbing mountains, or marathon running.

When discussing the attributes of a last, you will need to know the common terms.
The majority of measurements are volume rather than the traditional length and width associated with shoe fit.

A quick word about shoe sizes and grading. The size grade is simply how the last dimensions change as the shoe sizes increase. Every country has a different standard for shoe sizes.

The "size mark" does not truly relate to dimension of the last. A size 12 shoe is not twice the length of a size 6. In the USA size scale, each half size increases the length by 4mm, each full size, 8mm. The lasts' other dimensions such as waist width and ball girth "grade" at different rates per size.

Depending on the style of shoe that is being made, the last will need some special features to allow the shoe to release the last. The standard athletic shoe, with a floating lace-up tongue, can use a solid last. Loafers, oxfords, and boots will require a last that can articulate so the shoes are not damaged when production is complete and the last is removed.

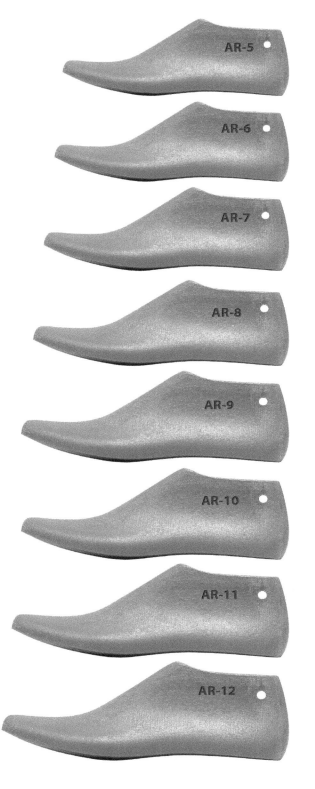

Solid shoe last: The most common type of shoe last, the solid last can be made of plastic, aluminum, or wood.

Hinged shoe last: The hinged last is often used for making fine leather shoes. The last can adjust to allow for easy removal.

Scoop last: In the scoop last, the instep is removable, allowing the cone of the shoe to be shaped.

Telescoping last: Used for high boots, the telescoping last separates into parts allowing the last to be removed without damaging the upper.

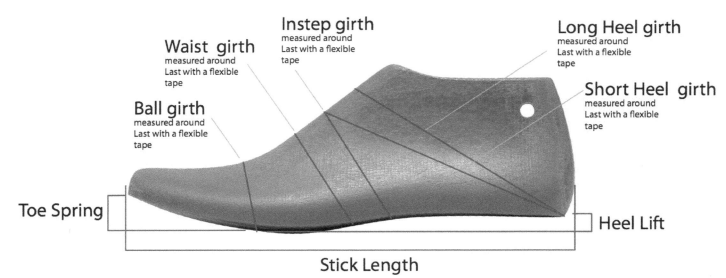

Shoe Last Stick Length: Measured from the longest points at the toe and heel.
Shoe Last Ball Girth: Measured with a flexible tape around the ball of the last.
Shoe Last Instep Girth: Measured with a flexible tape over the instep of the last.
Shoe Last Waist Girth: Measured with a flexible tape around the waist of the last.
Shoe Last Toe Spring and Heel Lift: Measured with the back of the last held parallel to the ground.

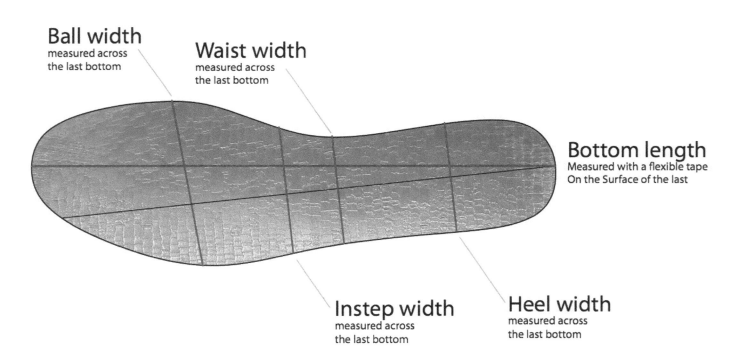

Last Bottom Length: Measured on the bottom of the last. A flexible tape is pressed to the surface.
Last Ball Width: Measured with a flexible tape across the ball of the last.
Last Instep Width: Measured with a flexible tape over the instep of the last.
Last Waist Width: Measured with a flexible tape across the waist of the last.

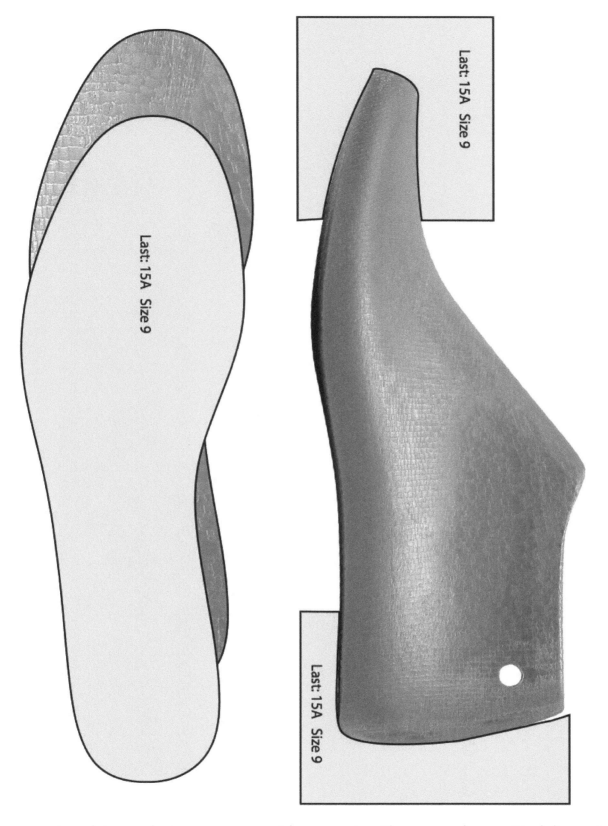

Last: 15A  Size 9

Last: 15A  Size 9

Last: 15A  Size 9

Heavy paper templates, or last gauges, are cut by computer. The gauges have critical dimensions marked, along with the last size and code number. The paper gauges are used to check each size of the sample lasts. Once the last fitting has been confirmed, the same paper gauges are used to confirm that all the production lasts are perfect duplications.

A set of last gauges can be used by the inspectors to make sure the production equipment is not worn out or damaged.

# Wooden lasts

**Pros:**
Easy to customize for a specific customer. Wood surface accepts nails and tacks required for custom shoe construction. Perfect for the handmade high dollar shoe or the handmade test last.

**Cons:**
Wood lasts are expensive, fragile, and susceptible to warping and rot if damp.

Do not agree with heat tunnels or vulcanizing ovens.

Not acceptable for modern mass production.

# Plastic lasts

**Pros:**
State of the art modern technology. Easy to shape and repair. Computer turned can be highly accurate for precision fitting. Easy to mass produce, impervious to heat and moisture. The workhorse of the modern high-quality sneaker factory.

**Cons:**
Can be expensive.

Durable, but can be chipped, dented and scratched.

Large sizes can be heavy and difficult for workers to handle.

Do not agree with vulcanizing ovens.

Expensive to recycle.

# Aluminum lasts

**Pros:**
Cheap! Easy to mass produce. Impervious to heat and moisture. Required for vulcanized shoe production. Perfect for short production runs. Easy to recycle. Light weight. Very durable.

**Cons:**
Shape is not as accurate as wood or plastic.

Not so easy to keep clean.

Quality can be suspect. Variation between sizes must be watched.

Rough surface can damage linings.

Plastic "blank" lasts waiting to be computer cut.

Here, the plastic blanks are rough cut at high speed.

146

These are turned plastic lasts used as master patterns to make the cast metal lasts.

One pair of each size. A busy last shop will have thousands of patterns.

Cast mold halves for the inner cores.

Pressed sand cores waiting for their turn in the mold.

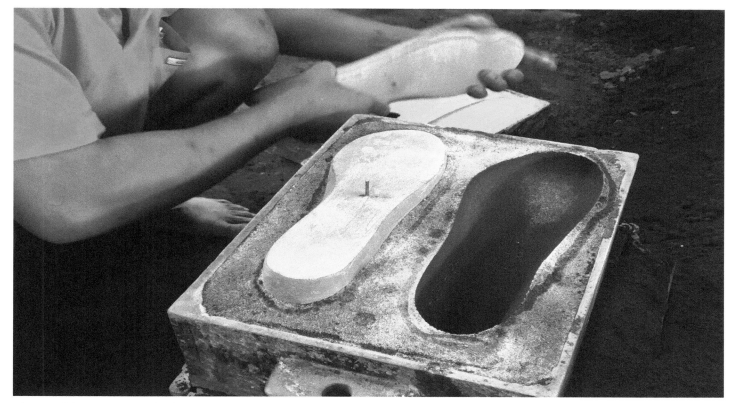

The mold is now ready for the sand core. The core will make the finished last hollow.

The worker lowers the sand core down into the mold by letting out a thread or plastic ribbon.

Here is the assembled mold. The hole in the top is where the molten metal is poured.

Red hot molten aluminum is scooped out with a long handle bucket. Note the scraps ready to go back in.

The metal is poured into the sand mold.

Just a few minutes after pouring, the mold can be turned over and the case split open.
The last is removed and the sand shaken out. Next, the molding sprue will be cut off and the lasts will be polished.

The technician is checking the length, bottom outline, toe, and heel curves. On the wall is the last grading specifications. You can also see the needle gauge used to check contours.

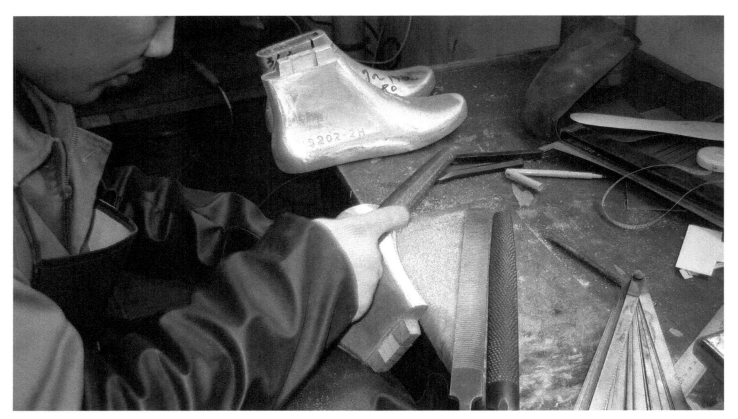

The lasts are now ready for finishing. Metal flash and imperfections are filed off. The lasts must be smoothed so there are no rough edges to damage the shoes during assembly. You can see the lasts' size and code number.

These workers have a lot of work to do. An assembly line will need 750 pairs of each last style to run smoothly.

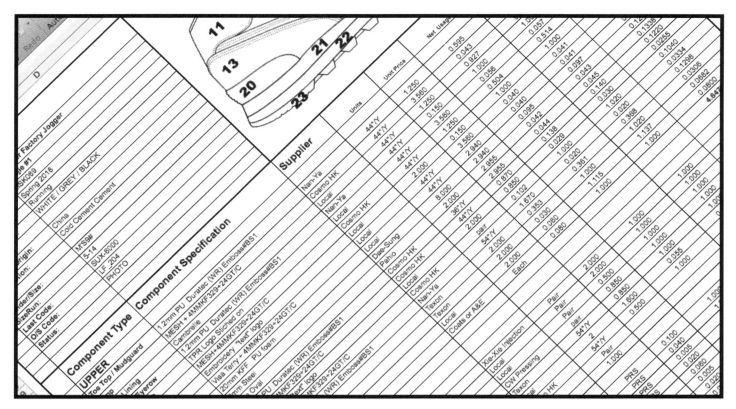

# CHAPTER 14

## FOOTWEAR COSTING

How much does it actually cost to make a sneaker? Is Nike making big bucks on those flash sneakers that cost $100? Let's break down exactly where the money goes.

Once the shoe is confirmed, the factory will take the spec sheets and detail the cost of each line item. This document is called the costing sheet.

The costing sheet will include every part of the shoe, including the box, stuffing paper, the silica gel pack, hang tags, etc. Everything in the shoe box must be listed.

Every item will be listed with its cost per unit and the usage needed to make that part. The waste percentage will also be added. The waste percentage, or cutting loss, is the amount of scrap material left over once the parts are cut.

Yes, you have to pay for the scrap that is thrown away. For mesh fabric, the loss is very small, less than 5%. In the case of fine leather for an expensive shoe, the factory can't use any leather with cuts or scars from the animal. The cutting loss can be 20%!

Next listed is the usage and waste percentage and the total cost per part. With each part listed, the costing technicians can check the material price for each part and measure the material usage. This is time-consuming work, but if the production run is 500,000 pairs, the pennies can add up fast. A diligent costing technician can save many thousands of dollars more than their salary.

The pattern cutting yield/loss is calculated by computer. The cutting yield can also be checked by hand with special graph paper and the paper pattern.

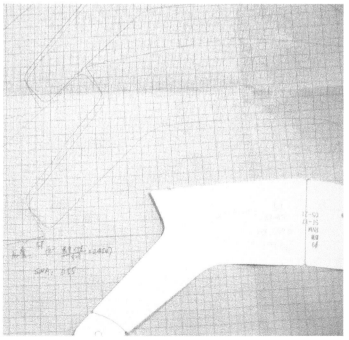

This is a common format for a spec sheet. The shoe parts are listed on the left with a brief note of the material specified. To the right side, you see the factory costing calculations per pair.

A costing sheet is a critical tool for the shoe developer and designer especially when they are designing a shoe to meet a specific price.

This will be turned into a costing sheet by the factory's costing technicians. (see next page)

The spec sheet on the right side of the page contains:

| Project Name: | Ariss Jogger |
| Factory: | Houjie #1 |
| Prototype ID: | ARJ-001 |
| Season: | Spring 2016 |
| Division: | Running |
| Color Description: | WHITE / RED / BLACK |
| Country of Origin: | China |
| Construction: | Cold Cement Cement |
| | Board Lasted |
| Gender/Size: | MS99 |
| SizeRun: | 5-14 |
| Last Code: | SUX-6000 |
| O/S Code: | LF_204 |
| Status: | Photo Sample |

| | | Component Type | Component Specification | White/Red/Black | Color | Supplier |
|---|---|---|---|---|---|---|
| | | **UPPER** | | | | |
| 22 | 10 | Toe Top / Mudguard | 1.2mm White Pebble grain Action Leather | White | | Nan-Ya Tanning |
| 23 | 20 | Vamp | Cosmo Dream Spacer 100% Polyester | White | | Cosmo HK |
| 24 | 30 | Vamp Lining | Cosmo Dream Spacer 100% Polyester | White | | Cosmo HK |
| 25 | 40 | Quarter/Eyerow | 1.2mm White Pebble grain Action Leather | White | | Nan-Ya Tanning |
| 26 | 50 | Quarter logo | TPR Logo "Ariss" | Red 187c/Black/Grey 2c | | Local |
| 27 | 60 | Tongue | Cosmo Dream Spacer 100% Polyester | Cool Grey 2 c | | Cosmo HK |
| 28 | 70 | Tongue Lace keeper | 1.2mm White Pebble grain Action Leather | White | | Nan-Ya Tanning |
| 29 | 80 | Tongue Logo | 32mm x 32mm Woven Label Stacked "Ariss" | Red 187c/Black/Grey 2c | | Local |
| 30 | 90 | Tongue Lining | Visa Terry + 4MM/KF329+24GT/C | Cool Grey 2 c | | Local |
| 31 | 100 | Tongue Foam | 20mm KFF  PU foam | NA | | Local |
| 32 | 110 | Lace Eyelets | 8mm Steel | Black | | Dae-Sung |
| 33 | 120 | Medial Vents | 8mm Steel | Black | | Dae-Sung |
| 34 | 130 | Shoe Lace | 8mm Oval | Cool Grey 2 c | | Pahio |
| 35 | 140 | Collar Underlay | Low Nap Suede 1.2mm | Black | | Local |
| 36 | 150 | Collar Panel | Cosmo Dream Spacer 100% Polyester | White | | Cosmo HK |
| 37 | 160 | Heel Logo | Print + Emboss 55mm ARISS | Red/Black | | Local |
| 38 | 170 | Heel Lining | Visa Terry + 4MM/KF329+24GT/C | NA | | Cosmo HK |
| 39 | 180 | Heel Counter | 1.2mm White Pebble grain Action Leather | NA | | Nan-Ya Tanning |
| 40 | 190 | Internal Heel Counter | Texon Rite thermoplastic 1.4mm | NA | | Texon |
| 41 | 200 | Internal Toe Puff | Texon Sportflex .35mm thermoplastic film | NA | | Texon |
| 42 | 210 | Eyerow Reinforcement | Super Tuff | NA | | Local |
| 43 | 220 | Upper Thread | bonded nylon 6  250D  3 Ply | Matching | | Coats or A&E |
| | | | | | | |
| | | **OUTSOLE UNIT** | | | | |
| 47 | 230 | Midsole Wedge Top | Hot Press EVA Asker "C"  45-50 | White | | Local |
| 48 | 240 | Outsole | #1-44  NBS400 Shore "A" 65  +or-3  SG 1.1 +1.4 | Black | | CW Pressing |
| 49 | 250 | Outsole Color Break | NBS400 Shore "A" 65  +or-3  SG 1.1 +1.4 | Red | | CW Pressing |
| 50 | 260 | Outsole Logo | "ARISS"  Logo  NBS400 Shore "A" 65  +or-3  SG 1.1 +1.4 | Red | | CW Pressing |
| 51 | 270 | Outsole Tip Stitching | bonded nylon 6  850D  3 Ply | Red | | Coats or A&E |
| 52 | 280 | Insole Strobal | Texon T28 | White | | Texon |
| 53 | 290 | Footbed | Cold Pressed EVA Asker "C"  45  Standard Open Mold | Black | | Local |
| 54 | 300 | Footbed Skin | Cosmo Hex Weave | White | | Cosmo HK |
| 55 | 310 | Footbed Logo | Screen Print Logo "ARISS"  65mm Heat Transfer | Black / Red | | Local |
| 56 | 320 | Cement | Water based PU | Clear | | Nan-Pou |
| | | | | | | |
| | | **PACKING** | | | | |
| 60 | 330 | Inner Box | 2016  Box art  E-Flue - White Back PVC skin | Red | | La-Wah |
| 61 | 340 | Out Carton | Brown | Brown | | Local |
| 62 | 350 | Tongue label | 3cm x 3cm White + Black Screen + Weld | Black / White | | Local |
| 63 | 360 | EEC label | 2cm x 2cm  White + Black Print | Black / White | | Local |
| 64 | 370 | HangTag | 4-Color Print | Color | | La-Wah |
| 65 | 380 | Tag pin | White | White | | Local |
| 66 | 390 | Wrap Tissue | 10 gram  2 sheets | White | | Local |
| 67 | 400 | Toe Tissue | 10 gram  2 sheets | White | | Local |

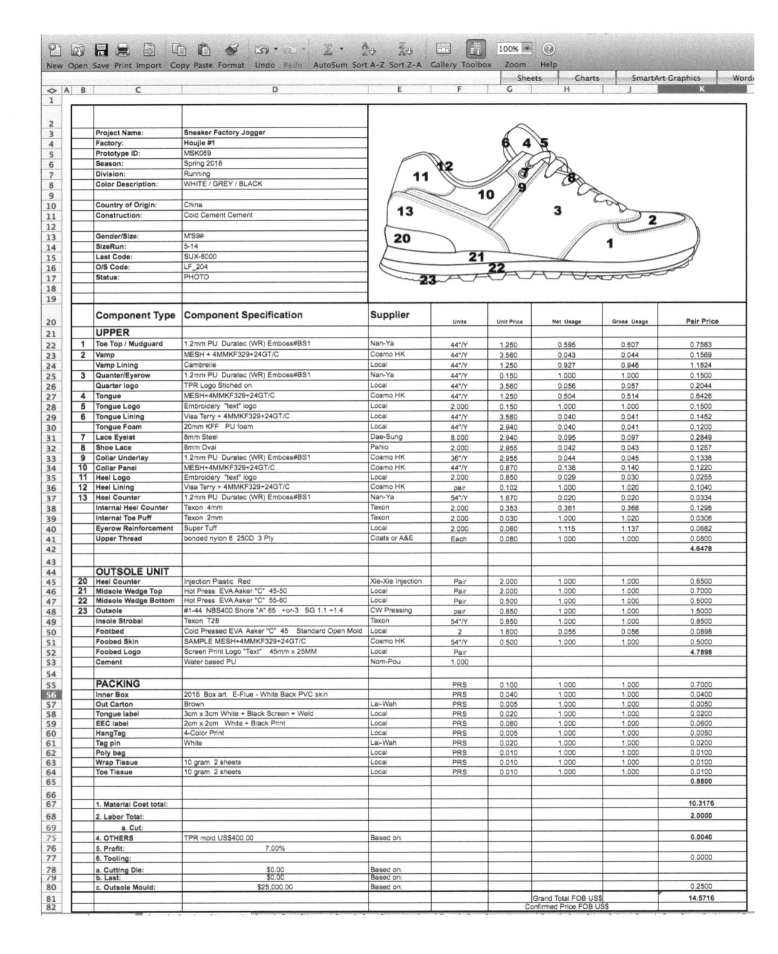

| Project Name: | Sneaker Factory Jogger |
| Factory: | Houjie #1 |
| Prototype ID: | MSK069 |
| Season: | Spring 2018 |
| Division: | Running |
| Color Description: | WHITE / GREY / BLACK |
| Country of Origin: | China |
| Construction: | Cold Cement Cement |
| Gender/Size: | M'S9# |
| SizeRun: | 5-14 |
| Last Code: | SUX-6000 |
| O/S Code: | LF_204 |
| Status: | PHOTO |

| | Component Type | Component Specification | Supplier | Units | Unit Price | Net Usage | Gross Usage | Pair Price |
|---|---|---|---|---|---|---|---|---|
| | **UPPER** | | | | | | | |
| 1 | Toe Top / Mudguard | 1.2mm PU Duratec (WR) Emboss#BS1 | Nan-Ya | 44"/Y | 1.250 | 0.595 | 0.607 | 0.7583 |
| 2 | Vamp | MESH + 4MMKF329+24GT/C | Cosmo HK | 44"/Y | 3.560 | 0.043 | 0.044 | 0.1569 |
| | Vamp Lining | Cambrelle | Local | 44"/Y | 1.250 | 0.927 | 0.946 | 1.1824 |
| 3 | Quarter/Eyerow | 1.2mm PU Duratec (WR) Emboss#BS1 | Nan-Ya | 44"/Y | 0.150 | 1.000 | 1.000 | 0.1500 |
| | Quarter logo | TPR Logo Stiched on | Local | 44"/Y | 3.560 | 0.056 | 0.057 | 0.2044 |
| 4 | Tongue | MESH+4MMKF329+24GT/C | Cosmo HK | 44"/Y | 1.250 | 0.504 | 0.514 | 0.6426 |
| 5 | Tongue Logo | Embroidery "text" logo | Local | 2.000 | 0.150 | 1.000 | 1.000 | 0.1500 |
| 6 | Tongue Lining | Visa Terry + 4MMKF329+24GT/C | Local | 44"/Y | 3.560 | 0.040 | 0.041 | 0.1452 |
| | Tongue Foam | 20mm KFF  PU foam | Local | 44"/Y | 2.940 | 0.040 | 0.041 | 0.1200 |
| 7 | Lace Eyelet | 8mm Steel | Dae-Sung | 8.000 | 2.940 | 0.095 | 0.097 | 0.2849 |
| 8 | Shoe Lace | 8mm Oval | Pahio | 2.000 | 2.955 | 0.042 | 0.043 | 0.1257 |
| 9 | Collar Underlay | 1.2mm PU Duratec (WR) Emboss#BS1 | Cosmo HK | 36"/Y | 2.955 | 0.044 | 0.045 | 0.1338 |
| 10 | Collar Panel | MESH+4MMKF329+24GT/C | Cosmo HK | 44"/Y | 0.870 | 0.138 | 0.140 | 0.1220 |
| 11 | Heel Logo | Embroidery "text" logo | Local | 2.000 | 0.850 | 0.029 | 0.030 | 0.0255 |
| 12 | Heel Lining | Visa Terry + 4MMKF329+24GT/C | Cosmo HK | pair | 0.102 | 1.000 | 1.020 | 0.1040 |
| 13 | Heel Counter | 1.2mm PU Duratec (WR) Emboss#BS1 | Nan-Ya | 54"/Y | 1.670 | 0.020 | 0.020 | 0.0334 |
| | Internal Heel Counter | Texon .4mm | Texon | 2.000 | 0.353 | 0.361 | 0.368 | 0.1298 |
| | Internal Toe Puff | Texon .2mm | Texon | 2.000 | 0.030 | 1.000 | 1.020 | 0.0306 |
| | Eyerow Reinforcement | Super Tuff | Local | 2.000 | 0.060 | 1.115 | 1.137 | 0.0682 |
| | Upper Thread | bonded nylon 6  250D  3 Ply | Coats or A&E | Each | 0.080 | 1.000 | 1.000 | 0.0800 |
| | | | | | | | | 4.6478 |
| | | | | | | | | |
| | **OUTSOLE UNIT** | | | | | | | |
| 20 | Heel Counter | Injection Plastic  Red | Xie-Xie Injection | Pair | 2.000 | 1.000 | 1.000 | 0.6500 |
| 21 | Midsole Wedge Top | Hot Press  EVA Asker "C"  45-50 | Local | Pair | 2.000 | 1.000 | 1.000 | 0.7000 |
| 22 | Midsole Wedge Bottom | Hot Press  EVA Asker "C"  55-60 | Local | Pair | 0.500 | 1.000 | 1.000 | 0.5000 |
| 23 | Outsole | #1-44 NBS400 Shore "A" 65  +or-3  SG 1.1 +1.4 | CW Pressing | pair | 0.850 | 1.000 | 1.000 | 1.5000 |
| | Insole Strobal | Texon T28 | Texon | 54"/Y | 0.850 | 1.000 | 1.000 | 0.8500 |
| | Footbed | Cold Pressed EVA Asker "C"  45   Standard Open Mold | Local | 2 | 1.600 | 0.055 | 0.056 | 0.0898 |
| | Foobed Skin | SAMPLE MESH+4MMKF329+24GT/C | Cosmo HK | 54"/Y | 0.500 | 1.000 | 1.000 | 0.5000 |
| | Foobed Logo | Screen Print Logo "Text"   45mm x 25MM | Local | Pair | | | | 4.7898 |
| | Cement | Water based PU | Nom-Pou | 1.000 | | | | |
| | | | | | | | | |
| | **PACKING** | | | PRS | 0.100 | 1.000 | 1.000 | 0.7000 |
| | Inner Box | 2016  Box art  E-Flue - White Back PVC skin | | PRS | 0.040 | 1.000 | 1.000 | 0.0400 |
| | Out Carton | Brown | Lai-Wah | PRS | 0.005 | 1.000 | 1.000 | 0.0050 |
| | Tongue label | 3cm x 3cm White + Black Screen + Weld | Local | PRS | 0.020 | 1.000 | 1.000 | 0.0200 |
| | EEC label | 2cm x 2cm  White + Black Print | Local | PRS | 0.060 | 1.000 | 1.000 | 0.0600 |
| | HangTag | 4-Color Print | Local | PRS | 0.005 | 1.000 | 1.000 | 0.0050 |
| | Tag pin | White | Lai-Wah | PRS | 0.020 | 1.000 | 1.000 | 0.0200 |
| | Poly bag | | Local | PRS | 0.010 | 1.000 | 1.000 | 0.0100 |
| | Wrap Tissue | 10 gram  2 sheets | Local | PRS | 0.010 | 1.000 | 1.000 | 0.0100 |
| | Toe Tissue | 10 gram  2 sheets | Local | PRS | 0.010 | 1.000 | 1.000 | 0.0100 |
| | | | | | | | | 0.8800 |
| | | | | | | | | |
| | 1. Material Cost total: | | | | | | | 10.3176 |
| | 2. Labor Total: | | | | | | | 2.0000 |
| | a. Cut: | | | | | | | |
| | 4. OTHERS | TPR mold US$400.00 | Based on: | | | | | 0.0040 |
| | 5. Profit: | 7.00% | | | | | | |
| | 6. Tooling: | | | | | | | 0.0000 |
| | a. Cutting Die: | $0.00 | Based on: | | | | | |
| | b. Last: | $0.00 | Based on: | | | | | |
| | c. Outsole Mould: | $25,000.00 | Based on: | | | | | 0.2500 |
| | | | | | | Grand Total FOB US$ | | 14.5716 |
| | | | | | | Confirmed Price FOB US$ | | |

157

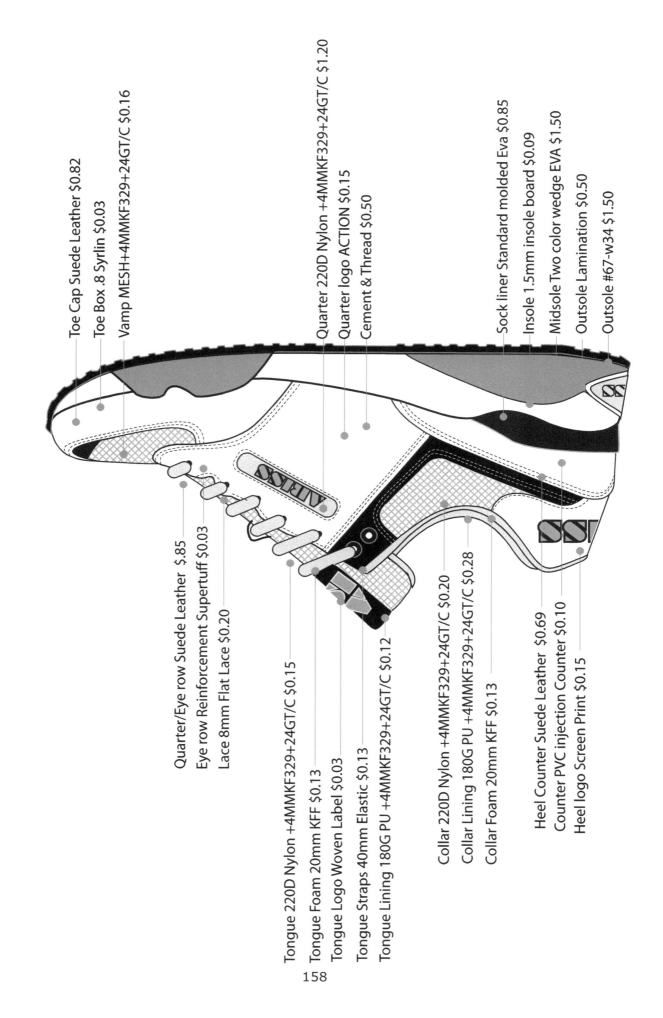

Toe Cap Suede Leather $0.82

Toe Box .8 Syrlin $0.03

Vamp MESH+4MMKF329+24GT/C $0.16

Quarter 220D Nylon +4MMKF329+24GT/C $1.20

Quarter logo ACTION $0.15

Cement & Thread $0.50

Sock liner Standard molded Eva $0.85

Insole 1.5mm insole board $0.09

Midsole Two color wedge EVA $1.50

Outsole Lamination $0.50

Outsole #67-w34 $1.50

Quarter/Eye row Suede Leather $.85

Eye row Reinforcement Supertuff $0.03

Lace 8mm Flat Lace $0.20

Tongue 220D Nylon +4MMKF329+24GT/C $0.15

Tongue Foam 20mm KFF $0.13

Tongue Logo Woven Label $0.03

Tongue Straps 40mm Elastic $0.13

Tongue Lining 180G PU +4MMKF329+24GT/C $0.12

Collar 220D Nylon +4MMKF329+24GT/C $0.20

Collar Lining 180G PU +4MMKF329+24GT/C $0.28

Collar Foam 20mm KFF $0.13

Heel Counter Suede Leather $0.69

Counter PVC injection Counter $0.10

Heel logo Screen Print $0.15

# When you buy a shoe for $100 were does the money go?

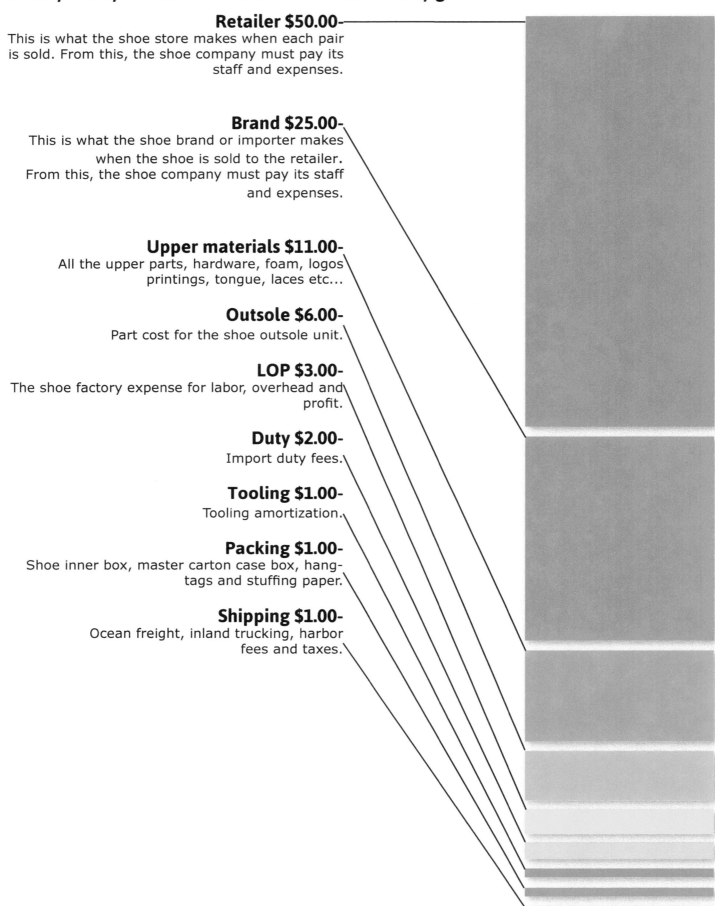

**Retailer $50.00**
This is what the shoe store makes when each pair is sold. From this, the shoe company must pay its staff and expenses.

**Brand $25.00**
This is what the shoe brand or importer makes when the shoe is sold to the retailer. From this, the shoe company must pay its staff and expenses.

**Upper materials $11.00**
All the upper parts, hardware, foam, logos printings, tongue, laces etc...

**Outsole $6.00**
Part cost for the shoe outsole unit.

**LOP $3.00**
The shoe factory expense for labor, overhead and profit.

**Duty $2.00**
Import duty fees.

**Tooling $1.00**
Tooling amortization.

**Packing $1.00**
Shoe inner box, master carton case box, hang-tags and stuffing paper.

**Shipping $1.00**
Ocean freight, inland trucking, harbor fees and taxes.

Let's start with the US retail price $100.00 and work backwards.

## Shoe retailer mark-up

The store buys the shoe from the shoe brand in bulk at the wholesale price, about 50% of the retail price, $50. If this is a big retailer, maybe they got a 3% to 5% discount or free freight to their stores.

The retail store just took 50% of the price!
Yes, but they have to pay the sales help, keep the lights on, advertise, and pay rent.
The store may also have to put a few pairs on sale. If the shoe is a slow seller, many may go on sale. When you see a "40% off sale" that means the store did not make any money.

## Shoe brand mark-up

Okay, what share does the shoe brand get? Remember, the shoe brand does not own the factory. Of all the major sneaker brands only New Balance has their own factory.

So, what did the brand pay for the pair of shoes they sold to the store for $50? About $20.00.

But, once the brand buys the shoe from the factory they still need to pay to ship it. Most shoes are shipped by ocean freight.

The terms for the price with the factory are usually F.O.B. F.O.B. stands for "Free On Board." It is the price of the shoe, plus delivery in a shipping container to the agreed upon port of entry in the USA or elsewhere.

## Landed cost

Freight costs from China to the USA are about $.95 per pair. A 40-foot shipping container, the size of a semi-truck trailer, holds about 5,000 pairs of shoes. 5,000 X $.95 = $4,750.

That cost will get a container from China to the USA, including port fees and inland trucking.

Once the shoe is in the USA, it must be legally imported. In the case of a textile running shoe, the US government requires an import duty of between 8.5% and 20% of the factory price. So figure around $25.00

Now the shoe is in the warehouse:
$25 minus $.95 minus $2.50 = $21.55

Now it's time to sell it to the stores:
$50 Wholesale Price minus $21.55 = profit of $28.45

Actually, it will be less than $28.45. The salesman gets a commission based on the wholesale price, usually about 7%. That's about $2.00 on a $50.00 shoe.

Now the profit is down to $26.45 per pair.
But wait, what if this is a big retailer that negotiates a 5% discount?

Take off another $2.00 to make the total profit closer to $25.00.

Of course, from that $25.00, the shoe brand has to pay the designers, product managers, developers, sales managers, marketing managers, advertisers, athletes, rent, taxes, etc.

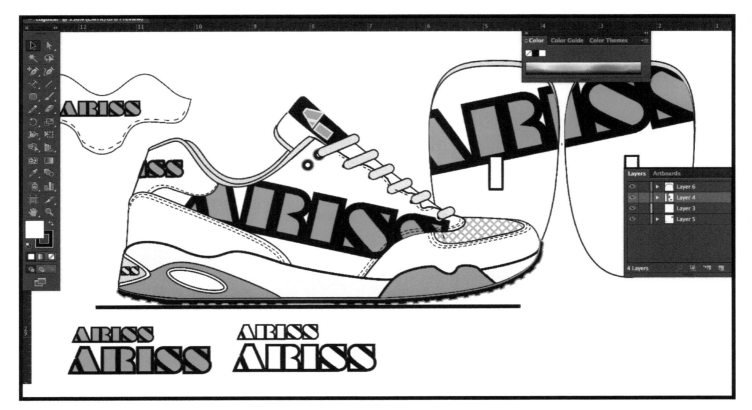

**CHAPTER 15**

# SHOE LOGO DESIGN

A new shoe design isn't complete until you have detailed its logos. A beautiful set of logos can add value, provide information for your customers, or be that unique and special twist. A great logo can provide the centerpiece for your shoe design.

When you are working with a new shoe factory, it is good to know their capabilities. For example, if the factory does not have an embroidery machine in-house, it will cost more to send the cut parts out for processing. Or, if the factory has a great relationship with the woven label supplier, it will be worth your while to arrange a visit to see what they can do.

Here we will review the most common types of logos found on sports shoes. We will discuss what the logo parts cost, set up charges, and designer tips.

Logo treatments can reinforce brand image, add interest, or communicate features.

# Die cut logo

A die cut shoe logo on the shoe quarter or side panel is the most common. The logo is simply cut out from a piece of material and sewn on. The Nike "Swoosh," Adidas "Stripes," New Balance "N," Vans "V," and Puma "Formstrip" are classics. Die cut logos are great for high visibility applications and can be made of almost any material. The downside is details can be limited to what can be sewn down. The die cut logo is a perfect overlay on top of any seam or pattern break. The die cut can also be reversed, so the logo is now a window to the inside of the shoe. Price is low, just the cost of the material.

# Die cut window logo

Instead of an overlay, the die cut can make a window exposing mesh or other logo treatment. Like a woven label or second color mesh.

# Cut weld

The cut weld is related to the radio frequency weld. The welding die has a crisp edge and when the TPU material is welded down the waste can be peeled away leaving behind the material. The colors and surfaces are limited to what you can get in the weldable TPU material. This is a great way to get a glossy logo on rough mesh or even better, chrome! The cutting weld tools may be $300 to $1000 depending on the logo size.

# Screen print

Screen printing is a very common logo application for shoes. Set up is nearly zero and colors are almost unlimited. There are many finishes available, such as matte, gloss, puff, or 3D styles. There are limits to the surfaces you can print on. Rough or suede surfaces will not print smooth. Elastic fabrics will cause the ink to crack. Any waxed or oiled surface is also not suitable for screen printing. However, printing is great for big, high contrast logos. Screen print logos can be several colors but watch out; registration can be difficult. Every factory will have a screen printing department. The logo can cost from $.25 to $.75 depending on the size and number of colors. There are not usually any setup charges for silk screen printing logos.

# Print plus emboss

An inexpensive and great logo effect for shoes. Achieved by screen printing, then using an RF welding machine to emboss the logo for a 3D effect. The RF welding machine is an inexpensive tool and the cut brass welding heads don't cost much. Inexpensive to set up, and when it's done in-house at the factory it's cheap! The emboss tools may be $300 depending on the logo size.

## Embroidery logo

Another very common shoe logo treatment. Embroidery or computer stitching can add a touch of class. Silky threads can create a rich looking logo application. Colors are limited only by your imagination; most machines can handle 8 to 10 colors! This is a great logo application but don't go crazy; embroidery is priced out by the stitch plus extra for more colors. The logo can run off the side of a panel part. Light colors can be soiled easily and/or threads can be snagged. If used in waterproof shoes be careful, the stitching will let water in. Price can vary wildly for this type of logo treatment, depending if the factory has its own embroidery department. There are not usually any setup charges. The logo can cost from $.25 to $.75 depending on the stitch count and number of colors.

## 3D Embroidery

This is a stunning way to make an amazing 3D effect logo. A small piece of EVA foam is placed under the embroidery head, the threads cut the edges when they are stitched down leaving behind a logo with a 2 or 3mm 3D effect. A great effect but prone to snags and soiling when used on shoes. There are not usually any setup charges. The logo can cost from $.25 to $.75 depending on the stitch count and number of colors.

## Back printing effects

Many shoes have plastic or rubber parts that allow the designer to add logos inside the shoe. Commonly, logos can be printed inside the clear rubber bottom of a shoe or added behind a semi-transparent mesh.

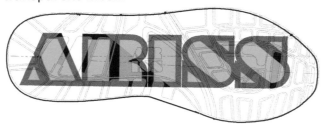

## Dye sublimation

Dye Sublimation is a printing process that uses a computer to print a full-color design onto transfer paper. When the paper is applied to the material surface and heated, the ink vaporizes and transfers to the shoe material. Dye sublimation is great for 4-color process photographic designs.

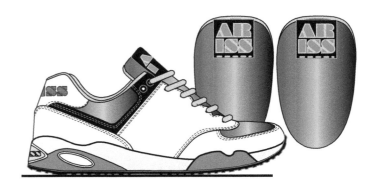

## Woven Labels

The woven label is another great way to create colorful logo effects. This type of label is machine-made by computer control. Resolution is high for fine details and small crisp text. Colors are nearly unlimited, and one logo can have as many as 15 colors. The basic tongue logos on New Balance or classic Nikes are made by this process. This process can be used to create informational labels on shoes. Setup charges are low, even zero. These woven label logos are not expensive.  Prices start at $.05 and run to $1.00 for a large multi-color patch.

## Chrome plated ABS

If you want a chrome logo you will need to go with metal or injection molded ABS plastic. ABS plastic has a unique surface character that allows vacuum metal coating so you can get a nice chrome plated surface.

## Molded logos

The modern sports shoe may have several molded components. EVA midsoles, plastic stabilizers, rubber outsole, etc. Each of these is an opportunity for logo branding your shoe design. These logos can cost you nothing once they are machined into the mold.

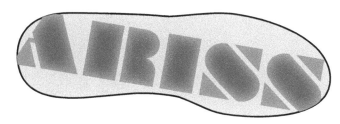

## Metal hardware

Metal hardware is a great place to get some custom logos on your shoe. Logo plates, custom eyelets, or lace fobs also give you another place to add your logo. This hardware can be cast, stamped, painted, plated, polished, or anodized. You will have many metal choices, from steel to brass, zinc, or aluminum. Custom metal hardware will have some setup charges. Price depends on the metal type and process required.

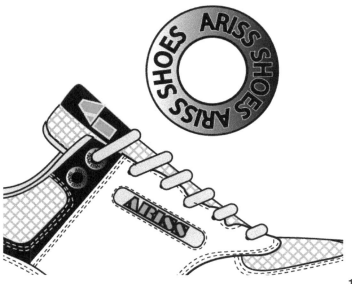

## TPR micro injection

Often called rubber badges, micro injection, or simply "TPR," thermo plastic rubber logos are a great way to add fine detail to your shoe's design. TPR logos come in all shapes and sizes. Details can be tiny, and colors are nearly unlimited. These little logos can be used as underlays or overlays, on tongues, and outsole bottoms. They are durable, colorful, and relatively inexpensive. ($.25 USD). They may have clear gel bubbles over them and can also have fabric backing. These are great for sports and outdoor shoes. One downside is they will require molds, luckily TPS molds are inexpensive and usually cost less than $200 USD.

## Pressed TPR

Pressed TPR is the high-tech version of the basic TPR logo. In this case, while the TPR material is still in the mold, the shoe material is laid into the mold. With heat and pressure applied, the TPR material is fused to the shoe material. This can be used to make small logos on large reinforcing panels.

## PVC Gel bubbles

A simple way to make a unique logo is the gel bubble. This is made by adding a clear PVC gel bubble onto a woven label, or printed sticker. These logos can have a stitch flange to use as an underlay or can be self-adhesive for attachment to midsole or outsoles.

## CHAPTER 16

# LEATHER FOR SHOES

Leather is the most common material used for making shoes. It is durable, flexible, stretchable, and available in many styles, colors, and prices. It is truly a great material; you can make beautiful, functional, and fashionable shoes! But, it does have some drawbacks. It can be heavy, hot, and susceptible to water absorption and damage if not treated. Water-resistant and water-proof treatments add cost. Leather is a relatively expensive material when compared to fabric or other man-made materials.

A well stocked sample room will have many leather hides.

Because leather hides are from individual animals, each is a different size and will have scars, imperfections, even brands that must be avoided when cutting. This uncut material is called cutting loss. For leather, cutting loss is at best 5%. For the highest quality shoes, leather cutting loss can be as high as 15%. That's 15% of the cost being thrown away.

Depending on the import rules for your country, leather is often a lower duty rate. Shoes made with 51% leather surface area are around 9% duty. A textile shoe can be 20% +$.90 duty depending on the country of origin!

## What is the best leather?
There are many different types of leather for shoes. Entire books have been written on the subject of leather and how it's made but we are just going to cover the basics for sport and casual footwear.

We are going to talk about real leather from animals! The most common is cow and calf leather, followed by pig, goat, sheep, kangaroo (for soccer cleats), alligator, ostrich, etc. We are going to focus on cowhide as it is by far the most common leather found in footwear and comes in many forms.

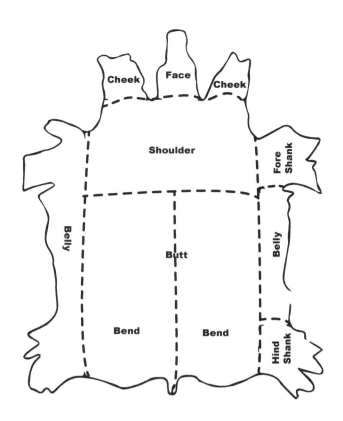

Leather is animal hide, during processing the hair is removed from the top or outer surface and any remaining flesh is removed from the inside of the hide. Following these operations, the hide is "tanned" or "pickled" to preserve the fibers. Other processes introduce fat to the leather to make it soft and pliable. There are many ways to tan a hide.

It is important to know that cowhide is thick and has two parts: the top surface or "grain" of the leather and the "split."

The grain is the most valuable part of the hide. The leather fibers are dense, tight, and firm. The grain surface is also smooth. There are many ways to process this type of leather depending on its quality. Full-grain leather can be processed to flatten the natural grain, treated to raise the grain, or embossed to have a completely different grain.

As the depth increases into the animal hide the leather fibers become looser and softer. These layers are called the "split," "split leather," "suede," or "split suede." It's called this because a huge metal blade is used to "split" off the top grain, leaving behind the suede surface.

166

Leather is tanned in giant rotating drums. During the tanning process the hides go through several different drums to treat, preserve, and dye the leather.

Once the wet processes are complete, the hides are hung out to dry before the final sorting and surface treatments.

# Common types of grain leather

## Full Grain Aniline

A leather which has kept its full-grain and has a naturally textured, full pored surface. The deep aniline coloring is achieved with soluble dyes and without covering the leather surface with a topcoat paint or insoluble pigments. It may or may not have a thin transparent finishing coat. This leather is the highest quality and the most expensive. Only flawless skins undergo such a treatment. Not well protected, these leathers darken well with age.

## Full Grain Pigmented

(also called Top Grain): This leather has also retained its full-grain but, on top of a penetrating dye, a opaque colored finish gives it a unified appearance, hides small defects, and protects the leather. Only high-quality raw-hides are used. This treatment makes leather pleasing to look at and to touch and makes it water resistant. It's the best compromise between aesthetics and resistance.

## Corrected and Pigmented Grain

To smooth out the leather surface and to eliminate its imperfections, wrinkles, and scratches, the skin is slightly embossed and a tinted grain film is applied to its surface. These leathers are not of the highest quality, and they have a slightly artificial appearance. The surface coating is quite resistant to heavy wear.

# Nu Buck

The velvety appearance of this leather is obtained by a light pouncing of the skin, thus highlighting the grain and the pores of the leather. To obtain a good looking nu buck, a quality skin is used. It's a pleasant material, soft to the touch, with velvety colors. Nu buck is fragile and requires a careful maintenance. A waterproofing treatment is mandatory. It remains a costly material. Nu buck can be oiled or post-treated. Thickness ranges from 1.8 to 2.2mm. Prices from $2.00 to $3.00 depending on color and quality. Lighter colors require higher quality raw materials.

# Crazy Horse

To make this style of leather a lower quality full grain hide may be brushed to remove just the top surface. The leather is then treated with a heavy, waxy, and oily compound that will darken the leather. This is the rough and rugged style of leather, and you may see scratches, bug bites, scars, and fat wrinkles in the surface, but that's okay, it's crazy horse. This leather will show color changes when flexed.

# Common types of split leather

## Split or Suede

Suede is a very common shoe material. It is the leather surface remaining after the top grain is removed. High quality, short nap suede, can have an appearance similar to nu buck leather. Lower quality suede may be hairy, cardboard-like, or a dusty off-color mess. Available in a rainbow of colors, quality suede is a stable material for casual, skate, and vulcanized shoes. Available in thicknesses between 1.2mm and 1.8mm. The most common suede is 1.4 to 1.6mm. Prices range from $1.05 to $1.45 per foot.

Pig suede will have a finer, softer surface. You can see the fine pores in pig suede.

## Pressed Suede

Starting with split leather, the surface is then treated with an oily, plastic-based resin. The leather hide is then pressed flat with an embossing plate. The surface will have a fine texture and may have a slightly glossy appearance. This is an inexpensive material, starting with lower quality hides. After some use the surface will crack and the suede fibers may show. This is not a good choice for fine shoes.

## Action or coated leather

This leather product starts out as a medium to low quality split leather. The surface may be pressed or rolled smooth. The hide is then laminated to a thin film of flexible, stretchable PU or PVC. This synthetic surface is made with colored resin, white and black are the most common colors. This surface will have an emboss made by pouring the plastic compound onto a sheet of textured paper. Once the film and leather are bonded, the split has a very smooth, full-grain like surface.

In fact, all the smooth white leather you see on sports shoes is this style of "action leather." This material is durable, waterproof, cuts clean, and behaves just like full-grain leather in shoemaking operations. Action leather is less expensive than suede, approximately $1.00 per foot. This material is also easy for the factory to cut and there are very few scratches or scars showing that must be avoided.

A very popular material for shoes, action leather is inexpensive, durable, looks good, and comes in many colors and finishes. Action leather can look like full-grain, nu buck, or glossy patent leather. Finally, despite its plastic coating, action leather is still considered leather for duty classifications.

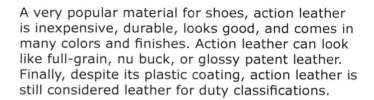

**CHAPTER 17**

# TEXTILES FOR SHOES

To design shoes, you must first have an understanding of fabrics. Textiles or fabrics are miracle materials for footwear designers. With an infinite variety of weaves, knits, colors, patterns, and special features, textiles have a special place in footwear design.

You will find fabric inside and outside footwear, even on shoe bottoms. The polymer fibers such as nylon and polyester are lightweight and durable. Lycra is stretchable, and cotton canvas is a must for vulcanized construction.

## Selecting textiles
When considering any textile for your shoe design, there are six features to consider:
thread size, fiber composition, weave pattern, backing material, sizing, and surface treatments.

## Thread size

The basic building block for fabric is thread! Denier is how thread weight is measured. 1 denier = 1 gram per 9000 meters of thread. Typical deniers are 110D for very lightweight fabric, 420D to 600D are thread weights commonly used for shoes, 1000D for boots and bags.

## Fiber types

Footwear textiles come in many fiber types including cotton, wool, nylon, polyester, polypropylene, rayon, and lycra. Each has their own look and physical properties like water absorption, stretchability, UV resistance, and color fastness.

For shoe design, polyester and nylon are very common. Stretchable Lycra and Spandex are often used for bindings and linings. Cotton is a must for vulcanized shoes as synthetic fibers will melt in the vulcanizing ovens.

Natural fibers like cotton or wool will accept finishing treatments. Cotton canvas shoe uppers can be salt or stone washed before assembly to give the shoes a special character. Cotton can also accept an oiled or waxed finish, but this must be done after the shoe is assembled. Oily or waxed canvas cannot be easily bonded to the shoe outsole during assembly.

## Weaves

There are many ways to "weave" the fibers together. In a woven pattern, two fibers cross each other. The fibers running the length of the fabric are called the "warp." The fibers running across the fabric, side to side, are called the "weft." The more typical "plain" square weave has an equal number of fibers in the warp and weft. There are many weaves: plain, twill, satin, basket, dobby and ripstop.

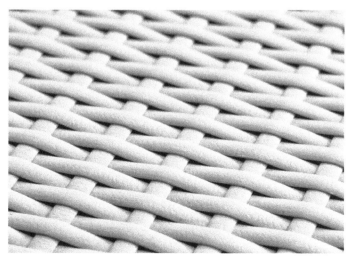

The "knit" is the other common way fibers are joined. In knitted fabrics, the thread follows a meandering path forming symmetric linked loops. These linked and meandering loops can be easily stretched in different directions giving knit fabrics much more elasticity than woven fabrics. Depending on the fiber type and knitting pattern, knit fabric can stretch as much as 500%.

Common knits types are jersey, interlock, double knit, and ribbed.

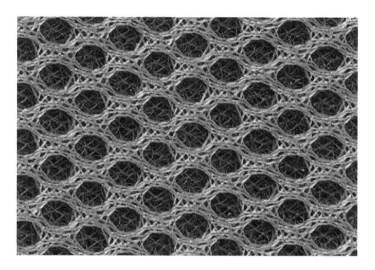

High-tech "Air" mesh or 3D mesh is made by knitting. Also know as sandwich mesh, the inner surface can be smooth and act as the shoe lining.

174

## Fabric backing and sizing

Once the fibers are knit or woven, the fabric must be dyed, sized, and backed before it can be used in shoes.

The freshly woven fabric is soft and shapeless, not suitable for use in shoes. It's the sizing and backing treatments that give fabric the toughness and body to make it useful. Sizing is a liquid resin treatment applied to the fabric. The fabric is stretched, heated, and treated with the sizing resin, and this holds the fibers in place.

The backing material is critical to the character of the fabric. There are two common backing types: PU and PVC. PU is a thinner, clear coating. It is cheaper, lighter, and not reliably waterproof. You can see the fiber under the coating. The PVC backing is solid; you cannot see the fibers through the backing. PVC is used to make a very sturdy, waterproof fabric.

Solid PVC or TPU backing makes the fabric very strong and waterproof. This solid backing is very common and a good sign of a quality product. The only downside is the weight of the material.

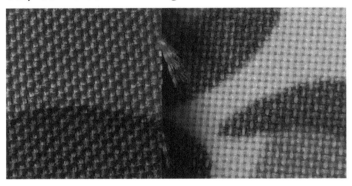

Thin, clear, PU backing gives the fabric some body and provides some waterproofing effect. It is light weight and not as durable as the solid coating.

Fabric Lamination: When fabric is assembled into shoes it is often laminated with a thin layer of PU foam. The foam backing controls wrinkles and makes the fabric easier to handle during assembly. The foam also prevents inner layers from x-raying through the thin fabric. This fabric has tricot material laminated to the back of the foam.

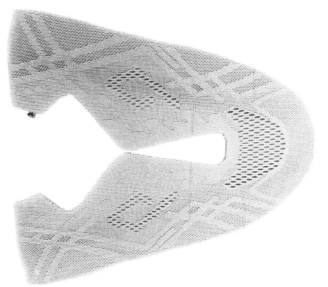

## 4D knitting

4D knitting is changing the way athletic shoes are made. A one-piece upper design is produced by CNC knitting machine, then assembled with the tongue, lining materials, and reinforcements.

This knitting technology, once found on only expensive shoes, is rapidly expanding to lower priced shoes. You can find this 4D knitting technology on running shoes made by Nike™, soccer shoes from Adidas™; even Chinese local market footwear is now being made this way. In the major shoemaking areas of China, the CNC knitting machine is becoming a very common sight.

To construct the one-piece upper, the knitting machine is loaded with polyester, nylon, or spandex fibers. The newest knitting machines can handle a mix of fibers and up to 10 colors at one time. The machine can be programmed to knit one upper or three uppers at a time with a maximum width of 90cm.

Depending on the programming and fibers selected, the upper can be thin and stretchable or thick and stretch resistant. The design opportunities are nearly infinite with multiple fiber options, colors choices, knit densities, and opening configurations.

The price is dependent upon on the number of colors and fiber types. A single color, polyester fiber design can be $2.50, while a multi-color, polyester/spandex combination can be $7.50 per upper.

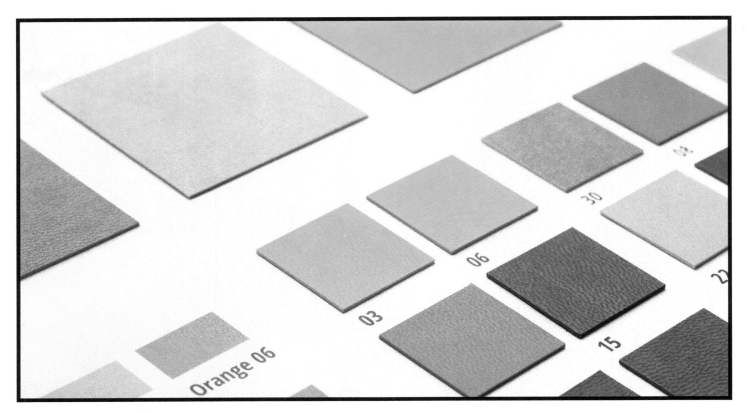

Orange 06   03   06   30   15   22

# CHAPTER 18

# SYNTHETICS FOR SHOES

Whatever you call it, synthetic, synthetic leather, PU leather, "pleather," or just PU, this material is another must-have for modern sports shoes. In order to design shoes, you must have an understanding of modern synthetic materials. This class of material offers the shoe designer a huge variety of colors, textures, and features at a range of prices.

While synthetics were once considered to be cheap junk not suitable for high-quality shoes, times have changed!

This shoe has a mix of synthetic PU materials. PU material can have metallic finishes and can be RF welded to create emboss effects.

## Synthetic material construction

Synthetic materials are now high performance and are often a composite made of two layers. A backing layer, made of woven or non-woven polyester fibers, combined with an external surface by "dry" lamination process or by liquid "wet" processes. The least expensive synthetics have a fibrous woven backing with PVC skin made by a wet process.

## Synthetic material types

There are four common surface materials: PVC, (Polyvinyl Chloride) which is the cheapest, PU, (Poly-Urethane) which can be higher quality with many surface options, TPU, (Thermo-Plastic Urethane) and a class of materials made of PU fibers without a surface skin. Of these four types, PVC and PU are similar in construction, a skin with backing. The TPU material tends to be a single layer material with a finer emboss. PU materials are offered as a solid, skinless material; this can have a brushed surface to look like suede or nu-buck.

## PU leather

High-end PU leather starts with a water-resistant microfiber PU backing. This backing has a smooth surface, cuts cleanly, and can be dyed to match the surface materials. The microfiber style backing can be ordered in .5 to 2.00 mm thicknesses and has some stretch. On top of this backing, the skin can be applied.

Polyurethane plastic film .2 to .5mm thick is made in a separate operation, and the two layers are then rolled together with heat and pressure. The PU outer skin is then printed, embossed, scuffed, or polished to create one of the millions of surface options.

The largest PU maker has hundreds of different embossing patterns that can be applied to hundreds of different surfaces. If you can meet the order volume required, you can pick any color you want!

PU leather is made with a sealed skin like full-grain leather but can be brushed to look like nu buck or fine suede. The PU skin is made by a release paper process but is dry when combined with the backing. A heated steel roller with the emboss pattern is used to laminate the skin and backing. This allows for a deeper, crisper emboss pattern.

The PU surface readily accepts embossing and printing effects. The PU skin is stretchable and durable so it can be combined with a lastable backing material. This allows PU to be used on the toe caps of sports and casual shoes.

PU material with high-quality non-woven backing

PU leather is also made in high abrasion versions and can have water-resistant backing. PU material with microfiber backing cuts cleanly and looks great when perforated. Backings can be color matched so cut edges look clean. They can even be ordered with accent colors for a neat "Tron" effect.

PU material can accept almost any emboss pattern. PU supply factories will have many textures available. The largest firms have hundreds of different options.

Any color and emboss combination can be made if the order is large enough.

## PVC Leather

PVC leather is the most basic synthetic leather, made by wet process, and the surface is a sealed skin usually embossed. Liquid PVC is poured on a textured release paper then a cloth is rolled on while the surface is still wet. PVC leather will often have a woven backing with limited stretchability. This is no problem for shoes with pieced together toe and vamp construction but not so good for smooth toe lasted shoes

This material is the cheap stuff found on inexpensive shoes. When it's pulled tight it may wrinkle and the backing surface will X-ray through the surface.

Perfect for cheap shoes, it can be found mixed on some shoes as a cost cutting feature. I would never spec PVC leather for shoes that retail for more than $75.00. Thickness ranges from .8mm to 2.00mm depending on the backing layers and surface treatment.

## TPU Sheet

Thermo Plastic Urethane or TPU sheeting is used to create seamless and stitch-less parts. The TPU is die cut, laser cut, or cut to shape while being attached to the shoe by RF (radio frequency) welding.

TPU materials can be used for both decorative and structural parts. TPU sheets can be clear, transparent, tinted, or opaque. TPU can be ordered in any color and almost any emboss texture. TPU is also available in sheets .3mm to .8mm in thickness.

## Synthetic suede

Synthetic suede, made of polyester microfibers, has a smooth, consistent brushed surface. Known as "Ultra Suede," "Alcantara™," Hi-skin, Chamude, Amara, Microfiber Synthetic Leather, these materials can be expensive but they are great for use on shoes, gloves, linings, and trim.

Available in thicknesses from .3mm to 1.5mm, synthetic suede cuts cleanly for detailed designs and is available in many colors. Being colorfast and waterproof, synthetic suede replaced suede in sports shoes that will be exposed to water.

the PU fiber backing materials are also made without the skin layer.

Decorative weld with red faux carbon emboss.

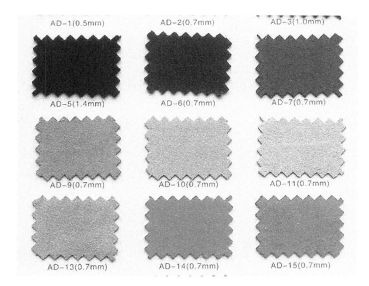

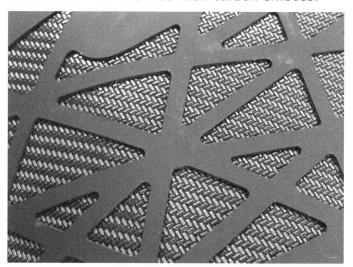

Laser cut .8mm TPU for a structural component.

**CHAPTER 19**

# FOAM FOR SHOES

There are many types of foam used to make shoes. Here we are going to review the types of foam found in the uppers of shoes and outsoles. Generally, foam is divided into two types, "Open Cell" and "Closed Cell" foam. These foams have different attributes to understand. Density, compression set resistance, and breathability are important to understand when selecting foam for your shoes.

## Foam density
Density, or Durometer, is simply how firm or stiff the foam is. For EVA foam, a density of 25"C" is okay for upper padding but way too soft for the midsole.

## Compression set
Compression set resistance is simply the foams' ability to bounce back after it's compressed. A foam with poor compression set will be crushed flat after just a few days.

# Open cell foam

Open cell foam is exactly what it sounds like, the plastic compounds that make up the foam cells are open, air and water are free to enter and exit the foam just like a dishwashing sponge.

Closed cell foam is exactly that, the individual cells are closed or sealed and do not allow the foams internal gas to escape. The stretchability and hardness of the plastic material, combined with the size of the cells, determines the density of the foam. Open cell foam is generally softer. This foam is made of Polyurethane plastic and is commonly known as "KF or KFF" foam.  This foam is available in different densities and in almost any thickness and color. It is used in the tongues and collars of shoes. Thin sheets of PU foam are used to back fabric in most shoe uppers. The PU foam allows the stitches to sink in and gives mesh some extra support while reducing wrinkles.

Reticulated foam is the most open style of foam. This type is often used for ventilation features. Reticulated foam is almost skeletal looking, air and water flow freely through the foam.

Memory foam is a variation of polyurethane with additional chemicals which increase its viscosity and density. Memory foam has a very slow return rate. Watch out; memory foam may freeze into a solid block in cold weather boots.

# Closed cell foam

Closed cell foam is denser. Midsoles of shoes are all made from this foam. The most common closed cell foams include EVA (ethyl vinyl acetate), PE (Polyethylene), SBR Styrene butadiene rubber), PU (Polyurethane) Latex and Neoprene. Each has their own properties. EVA foam is used for backing mesh materials, 2mm sheet EVA will make the fabric water-proof. Neoprene and SBR are used when elastic properties are required. Latex is common for collar linings.  PE foam is very light but not so durable.

When working with foam, it is important to know what foam is appropriate for the shoe upper and what is appropriate for cushioning the shoe outsole.

# How to measure foam density

Measuring the density of very soft foams can be difficult. The density is measured in lbs per square foot. Very soft open cell foam is 1.2 lbs per square foot.

For denser foam, a Durometer tester is needed.

An Asker "C" scale Durometer tester is used to test the hardness of foam shoe components. The Durometer tester will give you a reading of the density of the material. Try to test in flat spots, take several readings for each shoe part you are checking. For foam, try to cut the parts so you can test the center of the foam. EVA foam skin may give you a harder reading. A standard EVA midsole may be 55°, a soft footbed 35°.

A Durometer Shore A Tester is very important for shoe testing. The Shore A durometer tester is used to check the hardness of any rubber or plastic shoe component.

The Durometer testers bottom measuring pin is simply pressed against the material. Try to test in flat spots, take several readings for each shoe part you are checking. You can see the testing probe is very small.

# COMMON FOAM IN SHOES

## EVA (ethyl vinyl acetate)

EVA is the most common midsole material for sports shoes. It is lightweight, durable, easy to form, and resists compression set. EVA can be hot pressed, cold pressed, die cut, injected, and machined to make midsoles.

Available in a wide range of densities and formulations, EVA can be pillow soft and flexible, or rock hard and stiff. EVA can be made in almost any color. It can be found in all different styles of shoes. EVA is also used to make footbeds, padded stroble socks, and is often laminated as a fabric backing.

## Closed cell PU (Polyurethane)

PU is also a common foam for shoes. PU foam is "blown" into molds. The liquid compound expands and forms air cells to fill molds. It is used to make durable midsoles for hiking boots and can be made into entire sole units, which include the tread and midsole all in one. PU foam is used to directly attach midsoles to uppers. PU is expanded from a liquid allowing it to fill complex shapes. Many women's high heel outsoles are made from high-density PU. Very soft PU is used for footbeds due to is resistance to compression set.

## Open Cell PU (Polyurethane)

This foam is found in the uppers of almost every sports shoe. PU foam is open cell so care must be taken so that it does not absorb glue. Thin layers of PU are laminated to fabric to provide backing substance. PU foam is also used to make tongue foam and collar foam. Often called KFF foam. Due to its softness, open-cell PU foam cannot be used underfoot.

## PE (Polyethylene)

Expanded into sheets, PE foam is easily die cut and laminated. Parts are then pressed into shape for internal pads and tongues. Due to its weakness in compression set, PE foam is not used underfoot. PE foam is closed cell and waterproof.

## SBR (Styrene butadiene rubber)

SBR is a very soft foam often laminated between two layers of fabric. It is closed cell and is used to make parts waterproof. SBR foam is often used as a lightweight replacement for neoprene rubber but is not as stretchable.

## Latex rubber foam

Latex foam is easily formed into complex shapes in open top molds. Latex is used for upper padding but not as a midsole material. High-density latex foam sheets can be used to make die cut footbeds. The latex footbed provides excellent comfort for in-store effect but is not a durable foam for running for other athletic shoes.

# CHAPTER 20

## KNOW YOUR FOOTBEDS

The footbed, insole, or sock liner, is important to the fit, feel, performance, and cost of your shoe design. Footbeds come in all shapes, sizes, and materials. They may be removable or customizable or glued in. It's important to make the right selection to compliment your shoe design.

When a shoe is in development, it's important to have a plan for the footbed. Each shoe last will have a "sock allowance" built into the bottom, this creates space inside the shoe. The footbed can be 4mm or 6mm thick or more. You have to get this right, or your shoe won't fit quite right, then again, a little extra foam in your footbed can be used to fine tune or fix any fitting issues.

The footbed is also key to the lifespan of your shoe. A thin footbed, made of overly soft, cheap foam, can collapse after just a few days, leaving the shoe fitting loose and your customer with tired feet.

The ability for the foam to survive being placed underfoot is called its compression set or compression resistance. Not all foams are suitable for long-lasting footbed service!

Deep 3D molded contours make for a comfortable stable footbed.

## Common footbed types

Footbeds come in two construction types: molded or die cut. The molded footbeds are made of compression molded EVA, poured PU (polyurethane foam), latex & cork, sponge rubber, or PE (polyethylene) foam.

With a molded footbed you can add other features like injection molded stiffeners, support frames, gel pods, or airbags. The sky is the limit! But, you need to remember that a $4.00 footbed will add almost $20.00 to the retail price of your shoe!

## Molded footbeds

The molded footbed is the standard for performance athletic shoes. The contours will support the foot and hold the foot in place. Hiking, hunting, and military boots need a molded footbed. Inside strobel shoes, the footbed may be thinner as the inside of the shoe will have more contours from the last and molded midsoles. Stiffer board lasted boots should have a molded footbed to provide support and fill up the square corners created by a square edged last. Molded footbeds are usually removable.

Poured PU footbed; plush, long lasting, but heavy.

Compression molded EVA footbed, lightweight, inexpensive, and very common.

## Die cut footbeds

The die cut footbed can be the cheapest piece of junk or it can be super plush. Die cut does not have to mean cheap. Yes, the most basic shoes will have thin, die cut footbeds, made of soft EVA foam that will last just a few weeks. High end shoes can have really nice, leather-covered, die cut footbeds, made with multiple layers of high-quality long lasting PU foam, neoprene rubber, or gel sheet. Fashion and casual shoes can have die cut footbeds. Soccer cleats, even expensive ones, often have thin die cut footbeds. The die cut footbed is usually glued in place.

## Footbed cover materials

Footbeds can come with different cover fabrics or linings. The best fabrics have enough grip to hold your feet in place. Too smooth will not be stable, too grippy will ruin your socks. Running shoe and hiking boot footbeds need abrasion resistant materials to last for miles and miles. The footbed material must resist crocking (crocking is color transfer by friction or rubbing). Your shoes should not discolor your socks. Leather footbeds are nice, but may not be the best for athletic shoes.

## Other footbed features

Footbeds can be multiple densities of foam. They can have perforations or other venting features. Moisture-wicking fabric covers or bright graphics are a nice touch. Most companies will have their own molds with refined shapes and molded in logos. Another trick companies use is a very soft latex foam wedge under the heel. This latex will last for a while, but after a few days, or a week, it will be crushed flat. This is done to improve the "try on" or "in-store" feeling. For winter boots or hunting boots, you will find insulated footbeds with heat reflecting coatings. Shop around, try on many different styles of shoes, you will find lots of options. Let price, performance, and comfort be your guide!

**CHAPTER 21**

# MATERIAL SUPPLIERS

A supply of high-quality shoe materials and subcomponents is key to great looking and long lasting shoes. Your shoe material suppliers will be your best partners as you design and develop your shoe lines. A good relationship with your shoe material suppliers has many benefits. They can help recommend materials for your shoes, and they can also help you make or find new or unique materials. A supply factory with steady material orders from you will move your production to the head of the line or maybe more accommodating if there is ever a problem.

## Finding shoe material suppliers
A great place to start is your shoe factories existing material supply partners. Ask your shoe factory development department to order swatch books and sample cards for your study. They will have many leather, textile, PU leather, and plastic swatch books. Don't forget to ask for the price sheets! If they can't get you material books, snap a photo of the book so you can make contact yourself. If you don't see anything you like, don't be afraid to strike out on your own to find new suppliers! There are great material shows full of vendors looking for new customers. The Material Show and Alibaba.com are great tools for finding materials close to your shoe factory.

## Suppliers will come to you
Once you get started, a material supplier will be coming to you. If you work for a major brand, you may need to turn suppliers away! Long-term relationships with material supply reps are also a great way to get some "inside" information. You may hear your material rep say, "Oh yeah, we are making tons of this material for ....... and ......." Your material rep is also a great source of industry gossip. "Did you hear that so and so has moved to the new shoe company in Portland?" Keep your eyes and ears open!

## Visiting your material suppliers
When traveling overseas, make time to visit your existing material suppliers to see how they make their products. Supplier visits are always a worthwhile use of your time. You will gain insights as to the vendor's capabilities and processes. You may see something that peeks your imagination! A new machine, process, an old machine, a competitors material in production, there is so much to see if you are present in the moment.

## Local market suppliers

Depending on the location of your shoe factory, you may be close to local shoe material markets. These market areas are a great place to seek inspiration, and everything is for sale! Watch out for the material quality, make sure you test any local market materials before production.

## Shoe material selection

The materials you choose for your shoe design are what will make your design come to life. Rich leathers, silky mesh, or high-tech synthetics: you have an infinite menu of material choices and colors to create your masterpiece! However, great care must be taken to pick the right materials that can stand up to the demands of footwear. The demands of both footwear performance and manufacturing requirements must be met. A beautiful material that rips during the lasting operation cannot be used!

## Design factors for materials

When selecting materials for your shoes, your design brief should help guide your choices. The design brief should define the type of shoe you are making. A ballet slipper, or work boots for lumberjacks? Are these going to be inexpensive or premium shoes? With your design brief in hand and some background knowledge, you can find the right materials suitable for your design.

## A quick word about testing

There are many standards and tests for shoe materials. Tensile, elongation, bursting, dry crocking, wet crocking, flexing, abrasion, color fastness, etc. When looking at a factory's swatch cards, you will see the testing data listed. Working with reputable material suppliers is a must. They will have testing labs and experience with material suitability for your footwear applications.

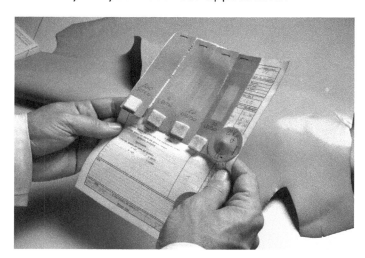

## Real Leather

Asiatan
www.asiatan.com

Wei Tai Leather Co., Ltd
www.weitai.cn

Wolverine Leathers
www.wolverineleathers.com

Auburn Leather
www.auburnleather.com

## Synthetic leather

Baiksan Co., Ltd
www.baiksan.co.kr

Clarino
www.clarino-am.com/

Nan Ya Plastics Corporation
www.npc.com.tw

San Fang Chemical Industry Co., Ltd
www.sanfang.com

Yuan Feng Synthetic Leather
www.szyongfeng.com.cn

## Textile

Bu Kwang Textile Co., Ltd
www.bukwang.com/

Dae Young Textile Co., Ltd
www.daeryong.co.kr/

Faytex Corporation
www.faytex.com/fabricbooks.html

Ducksan Co., LTD
www.ducksan.biz

Yuan Ling Knitting Ind. Co., Ltd
www.yuanling.com.tw

Cosmo
www.cosmofabric.net

## Thread

American & Efird, Inc
www.amefird.com/

Coats Thread
www.coatsindustrial.com

## Shoes lace and trim

Paiho Group
www.paiho.com

Junmay Label Mfg Corp.
www.jmlabel.com

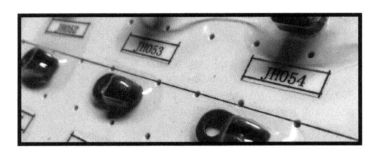

## Metal Hardware

Dae Sung Co. Ltd.
www.Daesung.net

## Footbed foam
Rogers Corporation
www.rogerscorp.com/

Ortholite
www.ortholite.com

Ultralon Foam
www.ultralon.co.nz

## Lining Fabric

Trendware
www.trendwaremarketing.com

Cosmo
www.cosmofabric.net

Yuan Ling Knitting Ind. Co., Ltd
www.yuanling.com.tw

## Outsoles

Jones & Vining, Incorporated
www.jonesandvining.com/footwear.html

Framas
www.framas.com/en/products/#c48

Vibram
vibram.com/

Meramec Group
www.meramec.com

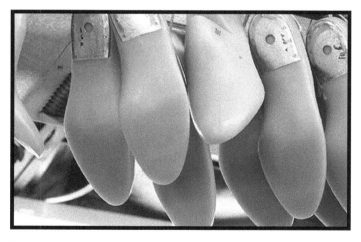

## Lasts

Jones & Vining, Incorporated
www.jonesandvining.com

Framas
www.framas.com/

The Shoe Last Shop
shoe-last-shop.com

## Lasting Boards

Bontex, Inc
www.bontex.com

Texon International
www.texon.com

TecnoGi S.P.A.
www.tecnogi.com/index.php/en/products

Cosmo
www.cosmofabric.net/

Jones & Vining, Incorporated
www.jonesandvining.com

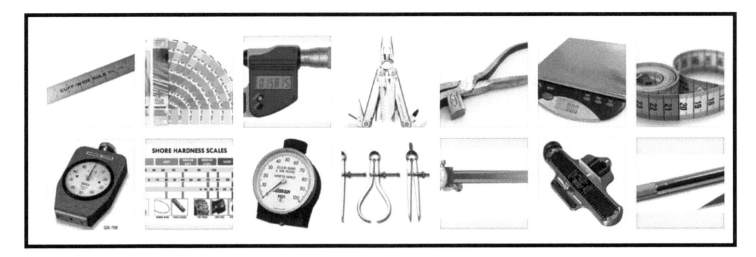

## CHAPTER 22

# SHOE DESIGNERS TOOLS

As a shoe designer or developer, you're going to need some shoemaking tools to help you do your job. Let's discuss the common tools a designer will use every day in a busy shoe design and development office.

Some of these tools are specific to shoemaking, others are commonly found. Of course, you will need computers and drawing equipment. Here is a list of the shoe designers tools that you might not regularly have but you certainly need.

## The Pantone system

Your new shoe is ready to be made, how do you explain to the sample maker in China or Italy the perfect shade of red you have in mind?

You could collect material swatches and cut color chips from around your office, attach these to your spec sheets and FedEx them to China. For unique materials or textures, this is a great idea. But, if you have 20 different shoes to spec with multi-color logos, this is not practical.
You also need to consider what happens inside the factory.

Your color swatch will have to be chopped up into a dozen pieces. One piece will go to the rubber factory, one piece to the mesh factory, one piece to the leather factory, one piece to the print shop, one piece to the shoelace factory, etc...etc... and, the main shoe factory needs to keep a piece to confirm the other factories get it right! This is not practical.
To save time and money, the professional shoe designers use a color matching system. There are several systems, Toyo (from Japan), Ral (from Germany) and Pantone (from the USA).

The Pantone color specification book is required for every shoe designer and developer. You will need to have a Pantone color book to communicate with the shoe factory and your customers exactly what color you want.

The Pantone corporation color books are the industry standard for color matching; you will find that every shoe factory will have a Pantone book, so it's easy for you to reference a color. Without the Pantone book, it's almost impossible to match colors correctly with your overseas factories. The books are expensive. You can share one in your office.

This is a must-have shoe designer's tool.

## How to use the Pantone System

There are many different Pantone books and chip sets. The basic color fans on paper are about $150. The two fan set is for coated (glossy) and uncoated (matte) finishes. The coated book is great for plastic, mesh, molded rubber, and PU leather. The uncoated book is great for cut EVA, synthetic nu buck, canvas, or any other matte finish item.

These colors are also available in tear out chip book format.

The Pantone company also makes the same colors in cotton, nylon, and plastic chips sets. For a big office, go for it! They also make an electronic color sensing system and many other color specifying products.

## A final note on Pantone books

When you get to the factory, have a look at their books. I was having trouble with one factory matching colors correctly, and during a factory visit, I found the printing department using the oldest, dirtiest, worn out Pantone book. AH HA! The manager was very angry when I took his book and threw it in the trash, but very happy when I gave him a fresh new one.

A Brannock™ device. You've seen this tool in every shoe store. This is the standard for measuring feet. If you're developing footwear, you must have a Brannock™ device in your office. When a tester says a shoe fits loose or tight, the first thing you need to do is measure their feet against the machine. Also, use your flexible measuring tape to measure feet. Make sure to measure both feet.

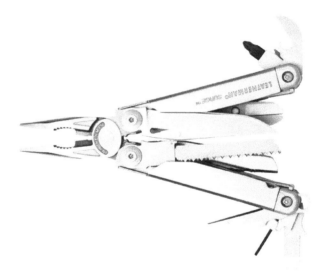

A Leatherman™ style multi-tool is a very useful piece of equipment. It has blades for slicing open seams and pliers for taking parts off. The serrated blade and saw blade are very useful for cutting sections out of sample shoes.

A pair of dial calipers or digital calipers is also very useful in making shoes. We use the calipers every day to measure the width of small shoe components.

An X-Acto™ knife is also a useful tool for cutting material swatches, opening up shoes and cutting open seams. A very sharp X-Acto™ knife is best.

A small steel ruler is very useful for measuring shoe parts. Make sure that the end of the ruler is cut off so it starts at zero and you can measure the inside of the shoe collar height by pushing the ruler into the bottom of the shoe.

Always have a flexible measuring tape on hand for measuring around shoe lasts and for measuring different shoe components. A flexible measuring tape is also useful for measuring feet and ankles.

A gram scale is also very useful in the creation of high-tech performance footwear. We quite often will have issues with subcomponents and measure each piece, part by part, to make sure that we're making the lightest piece of footwear we can make.

Shoemaking lasting pliers are also useful to have around. In the shoe factory they are used to pull the edges of the material down on the last. As a developer, you often use this tool to pull a shoe apart and see what's inside.

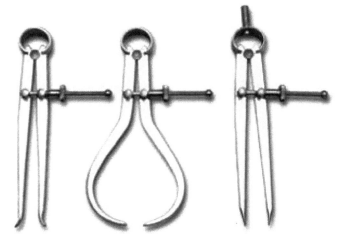

A set of adjustable dividers is useful in designing and developing footwear. Use the dividers to check critical measurements of lasts and different components that may be hard to reach. A pair of dividers is useful when comparing dimensions from one sample to another.

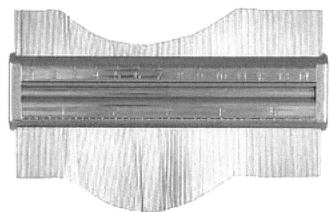

A profile gauge is nice to have when you are checking lasts. It's useful for checking complex curves quickly. While not a common tool, we use this when we are working up a new last or checking that a midsole is following the last bottom curve correctly.

A micrometer is a very useful tool to have in your shoe development office. We use this for checking the thickness of leather products or any synthetic material. We use a micrometer almost every day to confirm the materials in the sample shoe match the product specification.

A durometer tester is used to test the hardness of any rubber or plastic shoe component. The durometer testers bottom measuring pin is simply pressed against the material. The Durometer tester will give you a reading of the density of the material. Try to test in flat spots, take several readings for each shoe part you are checking.

An Asker "C" scale durometer tester is used to test the hardness of any foam shoe components. The durometer tester will give you a reading of the density of the material. Try to test in flat spots, take several readings for each shoe part you are checking. For foam, try to cut the parts so you can test the center of the foam. EVA foam skin may give you a harder reading. A standard EVA midsole may be 55°, a soft footbed 35°.

## CHAPTER 23

# JOBS IN THE SHOE TRADE

There are many shoe making jobs which do not require sitting in front of a sewing machine in Asia. Here are some of the common jobs you will find in a typical shoe development office.

## Shoe Designers

Someone has to draw the shoes. Depending on who you ask, this is the easiest part or the hardest part. The shoe designer has to draw what people want on their feet.

To be a shoe designer, art school would be a great help. There are many great design schools with industrial design, merchandising, and fashion design. A degree in industrial or product design is a great place to start. That said, if you can draw shoes like a bandit, who needs higher education? The designers draw the shoes, then work with the developers to make the prototypes just right. Picking color trends and knowing what is cool are critical skills.

## Shoe Design Manager

A successful shoe designer with best sellers in his or her portfolio will soon be asked to lead a team of designers. If you are a great shoe designer and have a talent for organization and leadership, you too can be a design manager. The footwear design manager is responsible for the training and guidance of younger designers and may also work to allocate projects, arrange inspiration trips, and work to motivate your team. The shoe design manager must also work closely with sales and marketing departments to review design briefs and schedules.

## Shoe Developers

It's the developer's job to take a drawing and turn it into a real shoe you can wear on your feet. The developer is the one that writes the technical specifications, checks the blueprints, and communicates with the shoe factory.

The developer's job is to get the shoe made and keep the free-thinking designers from making a beautiful shoe that is cruel to wear. Developers are the shoe prototype engineers and schedule keepers. To be a developer, you may start as a designer, an intern, or an assistant. Be ready to travel!

Landing a job as an assistant shoe developer is a great way to get started. You don't need any experience to get started. If you are willing to learn, travel, and work late calling factories in Asia, this is an awesome jumping off point!

## Footwear Development Manager

With a few years of experience as a shoe developer, you may be asked to take on more responsibilities. The development manager is responsible for allocating projects to developers, selecting factories for projects, scheduling development operations, solving technical shoemaking problems, designing tooling, managing advanced technical projects, sourcing new materials, and handling price negotiations.

## Advanced Technology Developer

Shoe designers and developers with a talent for technical details and a special imagination may join a team working on advanced technology projects. These projects may not be on any production schedule but will allow the shoe company to create new and unique designs. The advanced technology team will do patent research, visit new suppliers, and troubleshoot new production processes.

## Footwear CAD Technician

The design department will need computer-aided design support, and the tooling will need to be modeled to make molds. The shoe designers do not usually create the 3D CAD models, but instead will provide 2D or hand drawings to the footwear CAD technician. Depending on the focus of your company, you may have CAD technicians in your office or rely on your factory partners to create the CAD models.

## Footwear Product Managers / Product Line Managers

The product manager, or "PM," sets the designers and developers into motion. It's the PM's job to figure out what shoes to make and communicate these ideas to the designers. The PM is also responsible for working with the sales team and the customers to find out what they need. The PM is tasked with looking forward. What will people need next year? What color shoes will be trending? Experience in retail or sales is a big help. Shoe designers and developers can be promoted to PMs. A marketing degree will also help.

## Sample Coordinator

A busy development office will have hundreds of shoes coming and going. The sample coordinator is the traffic cop that tracks where the shoes are. Are the samples still in China? When is the factory going to ship them? Does FedEx need more paperwork to manage the import? When is the customer going to see their samples? The sample coordinator position is a great entry level position for learning the operations of shoe development.

## Sales Representative and Sub Rep

Selling shoes is a great way to get involved. The sales force is exposed to many aspects of the shoe trade. An active sales rep can help shape the product line. On the front line selling the shoes, the salesmen know first hand what customers are looking for. Salesmen can get promoted to product line manager positions.

## Working at a shoe store

Believe it or not, working in a shoe store is a great place to start for a high school or college student. Learn about shoes, meet the local sales reps, and sit in with the buyers when they review the new shoe lines.

## Footwear Retail Buyer

Working your way up the ladder in retail shoe sales can be a transition from selling shoes to a retail buyer. The buyer is responsible for making sure the store has the right assortment of the right shoes, at the right price, and right time! The footwear buyer for a sporting goods store will plan to have sandals and water shoes in summer, boots in winter, and new deliveries of shoes for the start of baseball in the spring and football in the fall. The buyer must study sales figures, have an eye for trends, and skills to negotiate discounts. Buyers usually start as assistant buyers, responsible for small categories, then move up if the shoes sell through fast without any closeout sales.

## Footwear Import Duty Classification Specialist

Any firm that imports shoes will need someone to help the development team and designers with product HTS duty classification. Without a classification specialist on hand, a shoe design could be 37.5% duty instead of 9% or 0% duty. The classification specialist works with the development team to avoid high duty classes whenever possible.

## Footwear QC Inspector

A proper footwear inspection program will have QC inspectors reviewing the shoemaking process from the beginning to end. Inbound QC is done when the shoes arrive in the USA. This QC inspection will ensure that there has not been any damage during shipping and catch any problems that may have slipped through in the factory. Usually, a trusted warehouse worker is given some basic QC training and then works with the development staff to resolve any questions. These inbound inspectors quickly learn what makes a quality shoe and will develop a knowledge of shoe construction. From this position, it's just a small step to become an assistant developer.

**CHAPTER 24**

# QUALITY CONTROL

## Footwear inspection procedure

All the effort to make shoes is wasted if the shoes are not made to a high enough quality standard. A careful eye is required at every step: cutting, stitching, and assembly.

All the major brands enforce strict quality programs with many inspectors at the factory.

## Shoe Quality Inspections: How to inspect a shoe

Once you learn how to professionally inspect a pair of shoes, you will never look at them the same way. Quality is a very important feature for any pair of shoes you make, buy, or sell.

Knowing how to run a shoe quality inspection is a critical skill for shoe designers, developers, and product line managers. When a new sample arrives, it is critical to inspect the materials, assembly technique and workmanship. Inspecting a shoe is a great skill to have as a shoe buying customer in a store. Here is how to grade and inspect a shoe like a professional.

# Definition of shoe inspection quality "A," "B," "C" Grades:

## "A" grade shoes:
Shoes without any functional or cosmetic defects to impair the marketability of the shoe. High-quality shoes which look good and fit correctly. An A grade must follow the production specifications and match the approved confirmation sample.

## "B" grade shoes:
Shoes without any major functional defects that could cause injury to the person wearing the shoes. These shoes may have cosmetic defects, production mistakes, or workmanship issues that cannot be properly repaired. These will be discounted and/or diverted to markets more tolerant of cosmetic defects.

## "C" grade shoes:
These shoes have major functional defects that could cause injury to the wearer or major cosmetic defects that cannot be repaired. Shoes are also considered C-grade if they have poor workmanship or material defects that could shorten the normal life expectancy of the shoe, or damage the company's reputation. C-grade shoes should be destroyed.

## How to inspect a shoe

The main points of an inspection are as follows.
#1. Is this the correct shoe, a matched pair?
#2. Is the shoe clean?
#3. Does the shoe follow the specification?
#4. Is the workmanship high quality?
#5. Is the shoe damaged in any way?

## Let's Inspect a shoe!

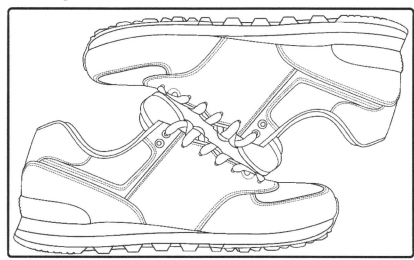

The first step in any inspection is to review the shoe packaging.
Is the shoe in the correct inner box for its model?
Is the box presentable? Make sure the box is not damaged or dirty.
Is the box the correct size? The shoes should not be crushed inside a small box.
Confirm the information on the box end label matches the shoe's color, model, and size.
Check any hang-tags to make sure they are correct for the shoe.

# Do you have a left and right?

Remove the shoes from the packing box.
Are the shoes the same size and color?
Check the shoe tongue label information.
In the factory, it's not hard to put a right size 7
and a left size 7.5 into the same box.

Holding the pair of shoes, place the shoes bottom
to bottom.
Check for symmetry. Does the pair match in
length? The size marks may match up but check
that they are the same length?

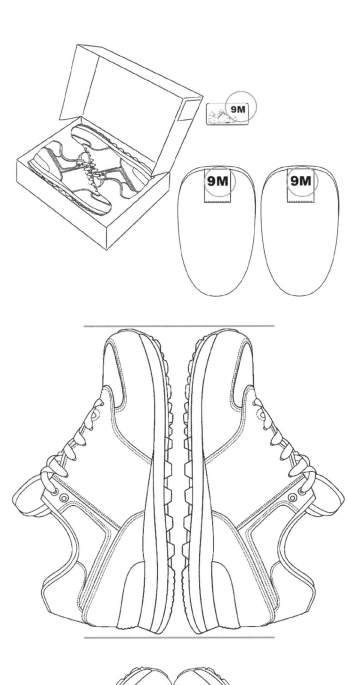

Now, holding the shoe from the bottom, roll the
uppers together side by side.
You are checking the alignment of the shoe parts.
Starting from the front, roll the shoes to align
the parts: toe caps, vamps, overlays, eye stays,
eyelets.

While you have the uppers side by side, compare
finish and colors of each part.

Next, hold the shoes up looking at the heels.
Make sure the shoe sits on the outsole straight.
Check that the upper is not rotated off center.

Next, rolling the heels together, check that the
back height and collar lines match.

Study the shoe bottoms, do they match? Are the
color blocks in the same location? Look over the
midsole sidewall for wrinkles. Check the seam
joining the upper to the outsole. Look for any
extra glue on the upper, 2mm is the limit for "over
gluing." Look for over buffing of the upper.
On the shoe bottom, check for color bleeding
between color blocks. Look for any paint covering
mistakes. Check to make sure the outsole parts fit
together neatly without any extra glue.

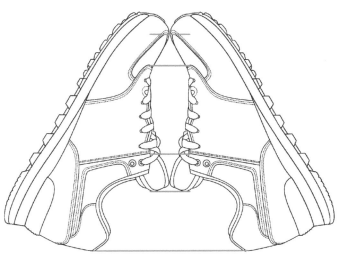

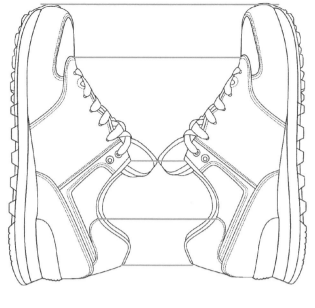

Now that we have looked over the outside, it's time to dive in. Look inside the shoe opening. Is the lining clean with no wrinkles? Run your hand around the collar, feel for any lumps, bumps, or glue. For leather shoes, be on the lookout for any lasting nails or staples. For sports shoes, make sure the footbed is straight, level, and fitting correctly. If it's too small, the footbed will slide around, if too big the footbed will be wrinkled or curled.

Next, inspect the tongue lining for wrinkles and lumps. Run your hand inside to check the vamp and toe cap from inside the shoe. Feel around the toe and along the footbed for lasting wrinkles. Feel for any rough stitching inside.

Finally, make a quick check of the laces. Too long is not usually a problem, too short, less than 6" above the top eyelet, will have to be fixed!

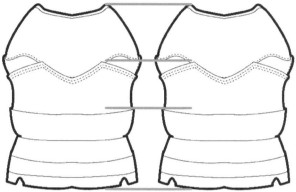

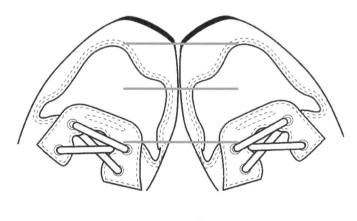

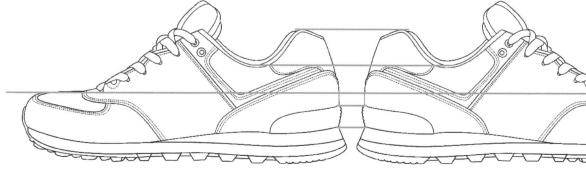

## Common shoe quality problems
When inspecting a shoe, there are common things you should be looking for:

Are the shoes clean? White shoes can be hard to make in a dirty factory.
Do the colors match? Suede and natural leathers can be tricky to match.
How is the material quality? Check for hairy suede or other material issues.
Is the cutting clean? Check that the trim and cut edges are not rough.
Are there wrinkles in the upper? Check around the collar foam.
How is the stitching? Check for crooked or broken stitches and stitch holes without stitches.
Do you see any pressing marks on the vamp?
Are there any dirty or smeared logo prints?
Did you review the seams? If you can see the stitches, this is called "grinning."
How is the lasting quality? Over lasting can pull seams near the toe apart or cause wrinkles.
Is there any rubber blooming? Look for white film on the rubber parts.
Do you see the rubber color bleeding?
How are the tongues attached? Check that they are not crooked and are attached at the same height.
Do you see any wrinkles on the foam parts?
Did you check for over gluing? Glue should not extend more than 2mm above the outsole edge.
Are there signs of over buffing? Buffing should not extend more than 2mm above the outsole edge.
Is there under gluing? Look for dry spots along the sole without glue.
Did you review the outsole? Check for any outsole parts splitting, cupped, bowed or crooked.

## A final word on shoe quality
When inspecting, it's critical to decide if any problems you see are a one-time mistake or a systematic problem that will effect every shoe. Remember, inside every factory, each operation is done by the same

Rubber blooming - chemicals inside the rubber are leaching out.

A toe cap over lasted. You can see the stitches are "grinning," like teeth.

201

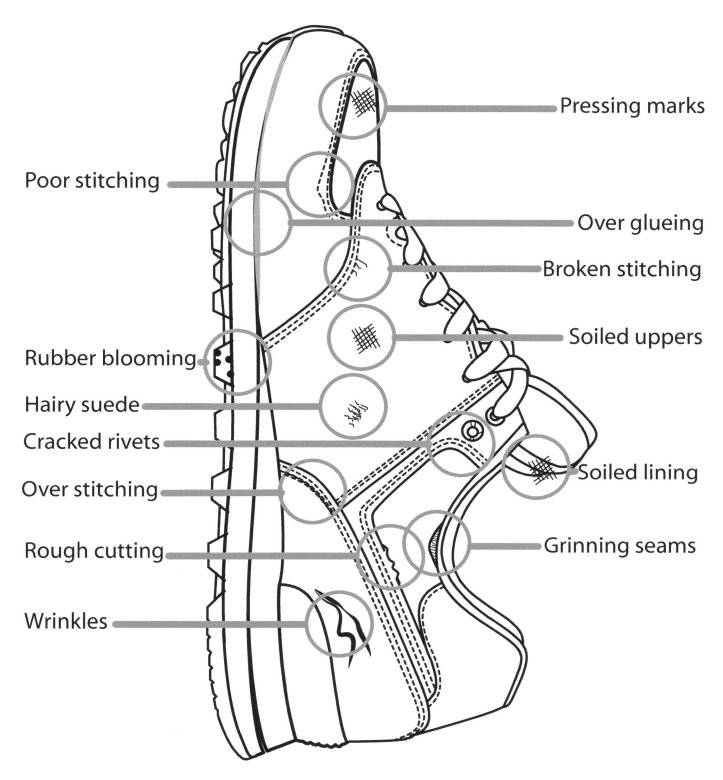

**Pressing marks**

**Poor stitching**

**Over glueing**

**Broken stitching**

**Rubber blooming**

**Soiled uppers**

**Hairy suede**

**Cracked rivets**

**Over stitching**

**Soiled lining**

**Rough cutting**

**Grinning seams**

**Wrinkles**

worker. If the vamp stitcher is having a bad day, you may see lots of crooked stitching on a vamp.

If you are inspecting "inbound" shoes inside your warehouse, you already own the problem. Ask yourself, "How did this shoe get this far? Who missed these problems inside the factory before the shoes shipped?" Heads should be rolling! Your factory has a QC system flaw. Can you "fix" your factory? Maybe you need to find a new one?

## CHAPTER 25

# LIFE AT A SHOE FACTORY

How are working conditions for the workers at the shoe factory? Working conditions at the export factories of major brands are generally good. Complicated, high-quality shoes can only be made in clean, well organized, well-managed factories by skilled and happy workers.

Remember, these factories are not owned by the big brands, this is ALL contract manufacturing. The big brands do set standards and run inspections but there are still some abuses.

The workers are paid an hourly wage according to China's national labor regulations and local rules. Factory workers make significantly more than the national minimum wage. Many positions require skilled workers and the higher the experience, the higher the wage.

Most workers are from rural western China and live at the factory in dormitories. They are provided three meals a day. Workers have health care plans, clinics, receive overtime pay, and have family leave. Child labor is illegal.

That said, you can still find many factories with poor working conditions and less than ideal human rights. If this issue is important to you, go with a larger, reputable shoe brand. Brands like Nike™, Adidas™, Reebok™, Under Armour™, New Balance™, etc. have rigorous standards, regular inspections, and only select factories that agree to follow the established policies.

Every year over 1500 people lose their lives in Chinese coal mines. The shoe factories are not bad by comparison.

An outside rest area.

Wide open streets lead to the factory buildings.

This dorm has basketball courts and a clinic.

Notice how clean it is.

This cafeteria feeds thousands of workers three meals a day. The cafeteria crew feeds the whole staff in two shifts.

New dorms under construction.

Lots of parking spaces for scooters. At this factory in Northwest China most of the workers live at home and commute.

## CHAPTER 26

# SHOE TERMS DICTIONARY

## Action leather
Sueded cow leather that is covered with a thin coating of Polyurethane. The coating may be any color and may be embossed with a roller. The final product is generally a solid color leather looking product. This material is still classified as leather for import duty. Almost all white sneakers are made with action leather.

## Aglet
The aglet is that little piece of plastic or metal on the end of the shoelace.

## Alcantara
Microfiber Synthetic Leather. This high-quality microfiber suede material can be expensive but is great for use on shoes, gloves, linings, and trim.

## Amara
Microfiber Synthetic Leather. This high-quality microfiber suede material can be expensive but is great for use on shoes, gloves, linings, and trim.

## Amortization or amortize
A factory manager agrees to let the customer pay for the shoe tooling piece by piece. By adding a small charge to each pair of shoes, the tooling cost is amortized. For example, a $10,000 tooling bill may be paid by adding $.50 to the first 20,000 pairs sold.

## Blow molding
The blow molding process begins with melting down plastic and forming it into a parison. The parison is a tube-like piece of plastic with a hole in one end through which compressed air can pass.
The parison is then clamped into a mold and air is blown into it. The air pressure then pushes the plastic out to match the mold. Once the plastic has cooled and hardened the mold opens up, and the part is ejected.

## Shoe cement bonding margin
The amount of space required to have a strong cement bond. If the rubber has only a 2mm bonding margin, the outsole may peel off the upper. A 12mm bonding margin would be better.

## Rubber BR-9000
Butadiene (Polymer) synthetic rubber made from petrochemicals, Rubber SBR1502
Styrene-butadiene (Polymer) is a common ingredient in synthetic rubber.

## Brannock™ device
This is the standard for measuring feet. If you're developing footwear, you must have a Brannock device in your office. When a tester says a shoe fits loose or tight the first thing you need to do is measure their feet against the Brannock device. The Brannock device will give you the length and width measurements. Remember to measure both left and right feet!

## Buff or buffing
To remove material by a sanding or roughing process. For example, EVA midsoles are buffed before assembly to help rough the smooth surface for better adhesion to the upper. The shoe factory will use a metal or stone wheel.

## Shoe cement or contact cement (glue)
Shoe cement is usually solvent or water based PU contact cement. Each part is coated with the cement and allowed to dry. The surfaces are then pressed together. Pressing is critical for a good bond. The PU cement cures in minutes, but a full cure may take days.

## Cement or board lasting
A lasting process where the insole board (cardboard or Texon board) is inserted onto the last bottom and the lasting margin (excess material of the upper) is lasted/pulled onto the board and cemented to the insole board. Shoes of this type are usually stiffer and heavier. A special machine is used to pull the upper and cement it in place.

## Chemi-sheet
A non-woven reinforcement material that is impregnated with a chemical hardener that sets with application of heat or another chemical. Used commonly for heel counter reinforcement on inexpensive shoes.

## Chamude
Microfiber Synthetic Leather. This high-quality microfiber suede material can be expensive but is great for use on shoes, gloves, linings, and trim.

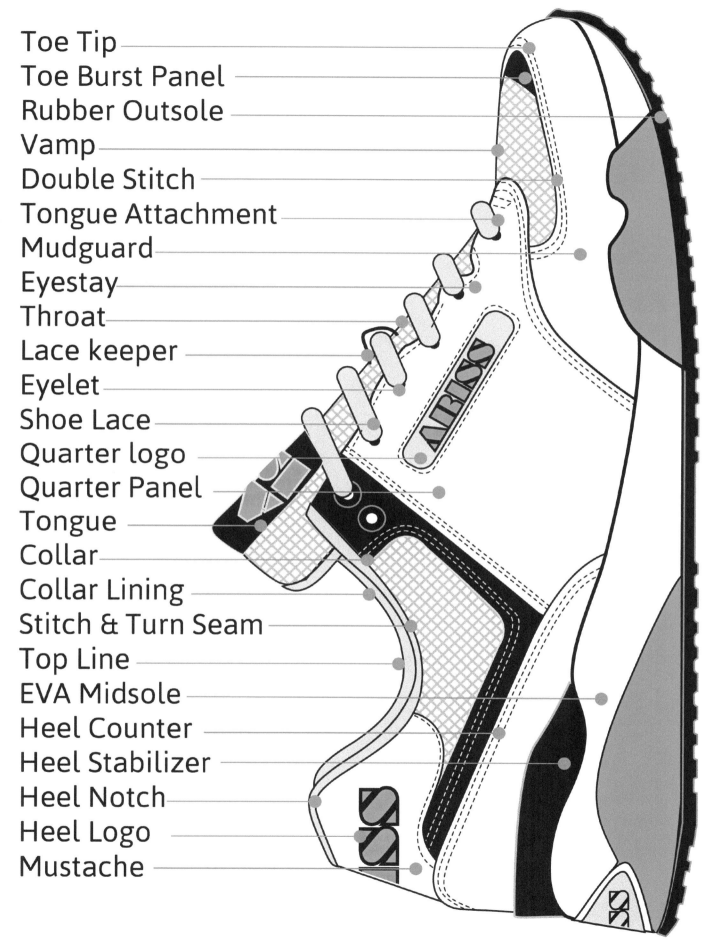

Toe Tip
Toe Burst Panel
Rubber Outsole
Vamp
Double Stitch
Tongue Attachment
Mudguard
Eyestay
Throat
Lace keeper
Eyelet
Shoe Lace
Quarter logo
Quarter Panel
Tongue
Collar
Collar Lining
Stitch & Turn Seam
Top Line
EVA Midsole
Heel Counter
Heel Stabilizer
Heel Notch
Heel Logo
Mustache

## Cold cement shoe making process

Bonding process to attach the upper to the outsole that does not require the upper to be placed in an oven. The outsole unit made of rubber and EVA foam is completely cured. PU cement, water or solvent based, is used to attach the sole unit to the lasted upper. Cold cementing does require heating tunnels to dry the surface primer and cement. Typically, the upper and outsole receive one layer of surface primer and two layers of shoe cement before they are fit together. Once the parts are fit together a hydraulic ram is used to press the parts, typically three operations from the top, sides, then front to back.

## Shoe collar or top Line

The opening area of a shoe at the top.

## Rubber sole color dam

A color dam on a shoe bottom is a raised ridge and/or groove in a mold to stop the flow of rubber. A sneaker shoe bottom will have color dams dividing all the colors on the sole.

## Colorway

A color/material combination. A model of a shoe may have many colorways.

## Compression set or compression resistance

For foam products in shoe manufacturing, we like to know how long foam will last if we build it into a footbed or shoe midsole. The compression set is how much a foam will bounce back after being compressed. Compression set is measured in a percentage. A foam that resists compression could have a score of 4%, a foam that is badly damaged by impact may have a score of 45%. Poor quality EVA will have a high compression set value. High-quality PU foam will last forever with a very low compression set.

## Shipping containers, ocean containers

A standard 40-foot long ocean container is the size of a 40-foot trailer on a semi truck. It measures 40' x 8' x 8' and holds about 5,000 pairs of shoes. There is also a half size, 20-footer, and an extra large 40-foot high cube (about 1 foot taller than the standard 40.) Top selling shoes are ordered by the full container load.

## Corrected-grain leather

Corrected-grain leather is any leather that has had an artificial grain applied to its surface. The hides used to create corrected leather do not meet the standards for use in creating vegetable-tanned or aniline leather. The imperfections are corrected or sanded off, and an artificial grain is embossed into the surface and dressed with stain or dyes. Most corrected-grain leather is used to make pigmented leather as the solid pigment helps hide the corrections or imperfections.

## Cosmo

The brand name of a common non-woven upper lining and reinforcement material. Used in all types of sneakers.

## Cupsole or cupsole unit

A shoe outsole type made of one piece of rubber. Called a cup sole because the sole unit "cups" the upper. Inside the cup can be EVA foam or rubber ribbed egg crate pattern.

## Cut and buff midsole

The cut and buff shoe midsole is the classic running shoe construction. The Nike Cortez and many New Balance classics use this assembly method. A cut and buff midsole is made by cementing a profile cut EVA to a flat rubber midsole. The profile of the EVA makes the toe tip thinner and the heel thicker. Once the EVA is bonded to the rubber, the parts are die cut to the correct outline shape. The assembly is taken to a grinding stone to have the side angle buffed.

## Shoe parts cutting

Traditionally called "clicking" or "clicker cutting," this is simply the cutting of shoe materials. There is an art to cutting leather due to the nature of the materials' grain. The cutting is done by a cutting die.

## Shoe part cutting dies

Used to cut out shoe parts. These steel cutting dies look just like cookie cutters. Each die is coated with rust proof paint and marked with the shoe size and model number. Making a shoe requires hundreds of dies. One die for each part on every size of a shoe.

## Cutting interlock loss

Interlock loss is the material lost when a big pattern part is cut. For example, a classic one piece hiking boot pattern can't fit closely on the hide. The material in-between the parts is lost.

## Cutting loss

Cutting loss is the material left over once the shoe parts are cut from a material. Depending on the material type the cutting loss can be 2% to 15%. The cutting loss also depends on the size and shape of the parts being cut. Mesh will have a low cutting loss; leather may be higher.

It's important to keep the cutting loss to a minimum as this loss will be added to the cost of the shoe. A skilled cutter will save the factory money!

## Cutting yield

When a large part is cut from a piece of material the cutting yield will be low. Conversely, when a small part is cut from a piece of material, the cutting yield will be high. Material that comes on a larger width roll will increase the cutting yield.

## Denier

Denier is how thread weight is measured. 1 denier = 1 gram per 9000 meters of thread. Typical deniers are 110D for very lightweight fabric, 420D to 600D are common in shoes, 1000D for boots & bags.

## Design brief

The design brief contains all the critical information for the footwear designer. Information like, who is this shoe for? What sport is the shoe designed for? What price is planned for the finished item? What country? A detailed design brief will contain much of the information the shoe designer will need to get started.

## Designers or shoe designers

Depending on who you ask, this is the easiest or the hardest job. The designer has to draw what people want on their feet. Designers draw the shoes, then work with the developers to make the prototypes just right. Picking color trends and knowing what is cool are critical skills.

To be a shoe designer, art school would be a great help. A degree in industrial or product design is a great place to start.

## Developers or shoe developers

It's the footwear developers job to take a drawing and make it into a real shoe you can wear on your feet. The shoe developer is the guy that writes the technical specifications, checks the blueprints, and communicates with the shoe factory.

The shoe developers job is to get the shoe made and keep the free-thinking designers from making a beautiful shoe that is cruel to wear. Footwear developers are the shoe prototype engineers and schedule keepers. To be a shoe developer, you may start as a designer, an intern, or assistant. Be ready to travel!

## Die cut EVA midsole

The die cut EVA midsole is a simple way to add cushioning foam into the bottom of a shoe. The shoe sole will have a cavity molded into the rubber. A piece of die cut foam is simply glued into the cavity. The die cut EVA midsole can be flat, or the EVA can be profile cut. This EVA is not visible from the outside of the shoe. It will be surrounded by the sole unit, and it will be under the lasting board or strobel sock.

## Die cutting

Most shoe parts are made by die cutting. The cutting die looks just like a big cookie cutter but has a sharpened steel edge. Each shoe part will require it's own cutting die.

## Double lasting

Double lasting is when a single shoe undergoes two lasting operations during assembly. The first lasting operation may be to pull a leather lining or a water-proofing lining tight. The second lasting operation would be for the shoe upper. Double lasting is often used to "hide" a molded foam midsole inside the shoe.

## Durometer

Durometer is the hardness of a material. You will need to specify the durometer of all the rubber, foam, and plastic parts. You will need two different durometer testers. Asker "C" is the EVA standard. 25 "C" is very soft, 55 "C" is a standard midsole, and 85 "C" is like wood. For rubber plastic you will need a Shore "A" tester. For a rubber outsole Shore "A" 55 is good. Above 60 your rubber will be stiff, heavy, and slippery. The durometer scale was defined by Albert Ferdinand Shore, who developed a measurement device to measure Shore hardness in the 1920s.

Shore 20A = Rubber Band, Shore 40A = Pencil Eraser, Shore 60A = Car Tire Tread, Shore 80A = Leather Belt, Shore 100A = Shopping Cart Wheel

## Egg crate rubber midsole

The egg crate pattern of square or diamond shaped walls may fill the heel of a solid rubber boot sole. This saves weight and allows for a sturdy sole unit. The egg crate may also be used to replace foam inside the midsole of an inexpensive shoe. It may also be used to level the inside surface of a rubber outsole to allow a sheet cut midsole to fit properly.

## EVA or CM EVA foam

Compression Molded EVA or Ethylene Vinyl Acetate. A foamed midsole material that offers good cushioning and compression set. Nike likes to call their EVA "Phylon," it is the same material regardless of the name you call it. EVA is the most common foam for shoe midsoles. Easy to form by cutting, molding, or injecting. It's light and durable. EVA can be made in many grades depending on the compound. More or less filler, more or less vinyl acetate in the mix. EVA foam can be made pillow soft or rock hard.

## EVA

Ethylene vinyl acetate is the copolymer of ethylene and vinyl acetate. The weight percent of vinyl acetate varies from 10 to 40%, with the remainder being ethylene. EVA is the most common foam used for shoe cushioning. It can be hot or cold pressed, made in any color and in a range of hardnesses.

## Ex-Works price purchase term

Ex-Works means the factory's price for the shoe does not include any shipping. The buyer would be responsible for collecting the product from the factory.

## Eyelet

A hole through which you lace up a shoe.

## Eyestay

The part around the lace opening (throat of the shoe). Can feature webbings, eyelets, etc.

## FOB "Free On Board" Purchase Term

In most cases, the shoe price will be stated as "FOB *port*" (the nearest freight harbor). In south China, it would be FOB Yantian. The seller is responsible for the inland trucking of the goods to the port of shipment, plus loading costs. The buyer pays for ocean freight, insurance, any duty or taxes levied, unloading, and transportation costs from the arrival port to the final destination.

## Footbed

Footbed, or insole, or sock liner. This is the foam padded mesh that your foot stands on. It may be removable or cemented in place. In high-end shoes, the footbed will be molded EVA or PU foam. In low-end shoes, it will be die cut EVA.

## Foxing tape

The foxing tape is the rubber band that makes the side wall of the shoe sole on vulcanized shoes.

## Full grain leather

Full-grain leather refers to hides that have not been sanded, buffed, or snuffed (as opposed to top-grain or corrected leather) to remove imperfections (or natural marks) on the surface of the hide. The grain remains, allowing the fiber strength and durability. The grain also has breathability, resulting in less moisture from prolonged contact. Rather than wearing out, it will develop a patina over time. High-quality leather furniture and footwear are often made from full-grain leather.

## Girth

The girth is the measurement around an object. When measuring a last you need to know the ball girth, instep girth, and heel girth.

## Glue allowance or glue line

The standard glue allowance is 2mm. The outsole glue may be applied up to 2mm above the outsole top edge. This allows a good bond. Too much glue can turn yellow later.

## Grade

Grade is the quality of the item. A-grade is good. B-grade has flaws and can be sold at a discount. C-grade can't be sold and must be destroyed or repaired if possible.

## Grading or size grade

Grading is making the different shoe sizes. Sample sizes for development are men's size 9 and women's size 7. Once the sample is confirmed, extreme sizes are made, size 5 and size 12. Then the remaining sizes are graded. The word is a noun and a verb. Can I see the size grade? Or, the pattern master is grading the pattern. The pattern grade is done by computer and then checked by the pattern master.

## Heel counter

Internal or external, the heel counter is the pattern part that covers the heel of the shoe. The internal heel counter can be made of rubber (for vulcanized shoes), thermoplastic (for cold cement shoes), chemi-sheet (for inexpensive shoes), or leather (for dress shoes). Depending on the shoe type, the counter can be thin and soft or stiff and sturdy.

## Heel notch

The heel notch is at the back of a shoe's top line, above the heel counter, the shoe may have a dip in the center.

## Heel lift

The heel lift of a shoe or shoe last is the dimension specified for the heel height above the ground. This is determined by the last of a shoe. A normal sports shoe will generally have a heel lift of 6 to 8mm above the ball of the foot. This is a standard ergonomic stance that will allow the shoe to have more cushioning under the heel. A casual shoe or sandal may have a lift of zero, and a high heel women's shoe last can have a heel lift of 4 inches or more!

## Heel stabilizer

The heel stabilizer can be rubber, plastic or leather. The stabilizer is bonded to the upper and midsole on the outside of the shoe as a functional and style part. Very common on the classic cut and buff style midsole type.

## Hi-Skin

Microfiber Synthetic Leather. This high-quality microfiber suede material can be expensive and is great for use on shoes, gloves, linings, and trim.

## Insole

Footbed, or insole, is the foam padded mesh that your foot stands on. It may be removable or cemented in. The insole for high-end shoes will be molded EVA or PU foam- and the insole for low-end shoes will be die cut EVA.

## Insole Board

A paper based board used to provide structure inside a shoe. For example, a stiff hiking boot will have a thick plastic lasting board. Also called sock liner.

## ISNR 20 (TSAR 20)

ISNR 20 (TSAR 20) is general purpose rubber graded by precise technical standards and not by visual characteristics. Some standards may vary marginally based on the origin. Technically, Specified Rubber (TSAR) is used for making tires, tubes, rubber mats, cushion gum stock, raincoat proofings, micro-cellular sheets for upholstery and packing, conveyor belts, footwear and various other rubber products.

## Lace Loop

Usually made of nylon webbing. A very common way to attach laces also called a ghilly loop. This style can be sewn under the eyestay to make a hidden lace loop.

## Last

The shoe last is the foot form that is used to set the shape of the shoes. The shoe last can be made of plastic, metal or wood.

## Last gauge

The pattern shape of the last bottom. This will usually be a paper card.

## Lasting

Lasting is the operation that stretches the shoe upper over the foot form or last. Almost all shoes are lasted in some way. With the last inside the upper, the outsole can be bonded and pressed into place. Once the outsole is bonded, the shoe can be de-lasted. There are several types of lasting operations: slip lasting, board lasting, toe lasting, waist lasting, heel lasting, string lasting, California lasting and hand lasting.

## Lasting board

A fabric or paperboard sheet used to make the bottom of the shoe upper.

## Lasting margin

The upper material part that folds over the edge of the last onto the bottom, overlapping the insole board. A lasting margin may be 15 to 20 mm.

## Lasting pressure

The lasting pressure is the amount of tension required to stretch the upper on the last form. Too much lasting pressure can damage, rip, or wrinkle the upper. Too little lasting pressure will result in a soft, ill-formed, baggy upper. It's up to the pattern master to get this right. Different materials will require different amounts of lasting pressure to look right.

## Lateral side

The lateral side is the outside or the non-arched side of the shoe.

## Letter of Credit, LC, term of payment

A letter of credit is a promise between businesses to pay. The buyers and sellers contract banks issue letters of credit as a way to ensure that sellers get paid as long as they do what they've agreed to do. The LC is common in international trade. LC is more expensive to transact than a wire transfer as it guarantees that a payment will be made if certain conditions are met.

## Linings of a shoe

1. Quarter Lining: horseshoe shape around back part of shoe
2. Vamp Lining: inside upper of forepart and toe of shoe
3. Sock Lining: covering all or part of the top surface of the insole.

## LOP or labor overhead and profit

LOP is a critical part of the shoe factory's price for a shoe. The factory will add up all the material costs, then add the Labor Rate, Overhead, and Profit required. The LOP for a shoe can be 30% of the total cost of a shoe. Just a few dollars for a simple skate shoe and up to $10 or $15 for a snowboarding boot. Some factories will add a percentage on to the material cost to account for the LOP. Other factories carefully calculate each component.

## The shoe master carton

The master carton or case pack for production shoes is usually a 10 or 12 pack depending on the size of the shoe and shoe inner box. In the master carton, the inner boxes will be arranged so the warehouse worker can see the shoe box end labels for size and color information.

## Medial side

The medial side is the inside or arched side of the shoe. The outside is the lateral.

## Midsole

The component of a shoe between the upper and outsole used to provide cushioning, fit, comfort and support. Will be made of EVA or PU foam.

## MOQ or Minimum Order Quantity

Shoe factories and material makers often have an MOQ based on dye lot size or machine operation. For example, a special mesh may require a machine set up, and thus the MOQ may be 500 meters. To dye a stock material may make the MOQ 50 meters. For suede shoes, the small dye drum load is 1000 sq. feet of leather. A basic shoe will use 2 feet of leather so a factory may request a minimum order of 500 pairs.

## MTO or Made to Order

MTO is a special production run of shoes. MTO shoes can be for a specific shoe store or international distributor. MTO usually require a special color or material treatment. The MTO product manager will work closely with sales managers, product line managers, sales reps, and designers to create new products. MTO projects can be brought to market quickly as there is no selling or booking period required. Once the design is confirmed the order can be placed to the factory.

## The shoe part: mudguard

The mudguard is the shoe pattern part along the forward part of the shoe along the edge of the outsole.

## The shoe part: mustache

The mustache is the part attached to the shoe above the heel counter. The classic sneaker will have a mustache.

## NBS or National Building Standard

NBS is a rating system for rubber wear. A typical rating would be 400, 800 or 1200 NBS.

## NR or Natural Rubber

NR is produced from latex obtained from rubber trees in plantations. The most important forms in which NR is processed are the following: Sheets, Crepes, Block Rubber and Preserved Latex Concentrates.

## Nu buck leather

Nu buck is top-grain cattle hide leather that has been sanded or buffed on the grain side, or outside, to give a slight nap of short protein fibers, producing a velvet-like surface.

## Ortho-lite

Ortho-lite is the brand name for a crystallized PU foam footbed. It is lite, flexible, and comfortable. This footbed can be found in high-end running shoes.

## Outsole or sole unit

The bottom component of a shoe that provides grip and traction. The outsole is commonly rubber but can be high-density PU or EVA foam. Dress shoes may have leather bottoms.

## Outsole channel stitch

The outsole will have a small groove or two molded into the rubber sidewall. After the shoe is assembled, a heavy duty stitching machine with a special bent arm is used to stitch a heavy thread through the rubber sole and the upper of the shoe. This channel stitch is often used on the toe tip of joggers, the side wall of skate shoes, and the bottoms of boat shoes.

## Overlay

An upper part which is over another part. The Nike swoosh logo is an overlay part.

## Padding

Refers to foam or other material usually inside the collar or tongue to add thickness/cushioning and improve fit. Usually made of polyurethane, latex, EVA, or PE foam.

## Pantone books

Pantone Inc. is a corporation headquartered in Carlstadt, New Jersey. The company is best known for its Pantone Matching System (PMS), a proprietary color space used in a variety of industries, primarily printing, though sometimes in the manufacture of colored paint, fabric, and plastics. It's the only way to make sure your colors are correct.

## Parting line or outsole parting-plane

The line in an outsole mold is made by the closing edges of the tooling. The tooling is split at the parting line. A mold may have one or two parting planes. Extra rubber may spread out of the parting line; this will need to be trimmed off. A narrow, tight parting line or parting plane is a sign of quality tooling.

## Pattern

The design of the shoe's cut parts. The shoe pattern is fit to the last. Designer and developers often make pattern corrections when creating a new shoe.

## Pattern cutting

Sectional patterns are produced for uppers, linings, insoles, heels, soles, stiffeners, backers, and toe puffs. The lasting allowance is added. The materials used in making the shoes are cut from these working patterns.

## Pattern maker or pattern master

The master technician that transforms the 2D drawing into a 3D pattern that fits the specified last. The designer draws the shoe; the pattern maker makes it into a real shoe. A good pattern maker can improve your designs. A rookie pattern maker can make a mess of your design!

## Pattern springing

To "spring" a shoe pattern is to transform the flat 2D shape in a pattern that can be pulled over a shoe last to make the 3D shape that fits the last tightly without wrinkles.

## Primer

Primer is a cleaning product, solvent, or water based product, used to prepare surfaces for bonding. The primer clears away any oil or mold released from parts which is critical for a good cement bond. During a cementing operation, both surfaces to be bonded will be primed before the cement is applied. Between each application, the shoe parts pass through a heat tunnel to quickly dry the primer. The primer must be matched to the material type. Rubber, EVA, and leather each require a different primer.

## Product managers or product line managers

It's the PM's job to figure out what to make and then set the designer and developer in motion. The PM works with the sales team and customers to find out what they need. The PM is also tasked with looking forward. What will people need next year? What color shoes will be trending? Experience in retail or sales and a marketing degree are helpful.

## Poly-Urethane

Poly-Urethane is synthetic (plastic) material with minuscule bubbles, or cells, and a skin like surface. Used for upper materials and for midsoles or padding foam.

## PU

Short for polyurethane. PU upper materials usually use a thin layer of PU foam with a non-woven or fabric backing for reinforcement and strength. PU can come in thousands of different colors and textures.

## PU Foam

Common padding inside shoe tongues and collars. Open cells allow air and water to enter. Can be very soft. Also known as KFF or K360 foam.

## PU leather

A man-made material, often a composite made of two layers. A backing layer made of woven or non-woven polyester fibers combined with an external surface by "dry" lamination process or by "wet" liquid processes.

## PU midsole foam

Another formulation of the Poly-Urethane material. In this case, foamed or blown into closed molds. Used for midsoles, footbeds, and some upper cushioning parts. Can be heavier than EVA but is more elastic and bendable. Heavy duty hiking shoes and work boots may have PU midsoles.

## PU Nu buck

A man-made material often a composite made of two layers. A backing layer made of woven or non-woven polyester fibers combined with an external surface by "dry" lamination process. The top PU surface is slightly brushed to make a smooth matte finish. This is very common shoe material.

## Pullover

A prototype sample shoe upper for checking pattern and fit. When a shoe is developed, the first thing you see is the pullover without an outsole and usually without logos or art. The pullover will not be made with color correct materials, but instead with any overstock color. During the development phase, you may make several pullovers to get the pattern correct. You will also see pullovers made of each size during the pre-production phase. The pullover will also be sent to the outsole factory to ensure the shoe bottom will fit correctly.

## PVC leather

A man-made material often a composite made of two layers. A backing layer made of woven or non-woven polyester fibers combined with an external surface by "dry" lamination process or by "wet" liquid processes.

## The shoe part: quarter panel

The quarter panel is the main shoe pattern part on the side of the shoe. The Nike Swoosh, New Balance N, and the Vans V-Bar are all located on the quarter panel.

## Retail price

The retail price is the price a customer pays in the shoe store for a pair of shoes.

## Roughing

To remove material by a sanding or brushing process. For example, EVA midsoles are roughed before assembly to help break the smooth surface for better adhesion to the shoe primer and cement.

## Rubber RSS 1

RSS 1 refers to Ribbed Smoked Sheets, produced from natural rubber latex as ribbed sheets, by coagulation with acids and sheeting, properly air dried and smoked, and visually graded.

## Sales representative and sub rep

On the front line selling the shoes, the sales representative and sub reps know first hand what customers are looking for. They meet with retail buyers and sell the shoes to the retail stores. The sales force is exposed to many aspects of the shoe trade, and an active sales rep can help shape the product line. A sub rep can get promoted to become a sales rep, and sales reps can get promoted to a product line manager position.

## Sample coordinator

A busy development office will have hundreds of shoes coming and going. The sample coordinator is the traffic cop that tracks where the shoes are. Are the samples still in China? When is the factory going to ship them? Does FedEx need more paperwork to manage the import? The sample coordinator position is a great entry level position for learning the operations of shoe development and shoe design.

## Sample size

Most commonly samples are made in men's size 9 and women's size 7. These sizes are well proportioned and look the best for sales presentations and print ads. Size 9 and 7 are also the fair and average size to use for costing. Larger sizes will consume more material, but the smaller sizes will consume less.

## Shell pattern

The shoe pattern that fits the surface of the last without any details. The designer may draw on the shell pattern.

## Sipes

A knife cut pattern on the bottom of a shoe sole, common on boat shoes or deck shoes. The sipes or "siping" pattern disperses water and prevents slipping.

## SKU or Stock Keeping Unit

A unique model/style/color-way/size. Commonly used to refer to a unique color-way. For example, if there are two models each with five color-ways, there are 10 SKU's total.

## Slip lasting

A lasting process where the insole board or Strobel sock (usually canvas or non-woven) is stitched around the last bottom edge to complete the upper. Usually used for lightweight and flexible shoes such as running shoes.

## SMU or Special Make-Up

SMU is a special production run of shoes. They can be for a specific shoe store or international distributor. Usually a special color or material treatment. The SMU product manager will work closely with sales managers, product line managers, sales reps, and designers to create new products. SMU projects can be brought to market quickly as there is no selling or booking period required. Once the design is confirmed the order can be placed to the factory.

## Sock allowance

The sock allowance is the extra material added to the last bottom to make space inside the finished shoe. Too little or too much will cause the finished shoe to fit loose or tight. A typical sock allowance is 4mm to 6mm.

## Sock or Sock liner

The sock, sock liner, footbed, or insole is the foam padded mesh that your foot stands on. It may be removable or may be cemented in. In high-end shoes, it will be made from molded EVA or PU foam. In low-end shoes, it will be made from die cut EVA.

## Split leather or suede leather

Split leather is created from the fibrous part of the hide left once the top-grain of the rawhide has been separated from the hide. During the splitting operation, the top-grain and drop split are separated. The drop split can be further split (thickness allowing) into a middle split and a flesh split. In very thick hides, the middle split can be separated into multiple layers until the thickness prevents further splitting. Split leather then has an artificial layer applied to the surface of the split and is embossed with a leather grain (bycast leather). Splits are also used to create suede. The strongest suedes are usually made from grain splits (that have the grain completely removed,) or from the flesh split that has been shaved to the correct thickness. Suede is "fuzzy" on both sides. Manufacturers use a variety of techniques to make suede from full-grain. A reversed suede is a grained leather that has been designed into the leather article with the grain facing away from the visible surface. It is not considered to be a true form of suede.

## Stitch and turn (seam)

A seam which is stitched to join two parts, then flipped inside out so the stitch is hidden. The stitch and turn seam is nearly always found where the collar of the shoe meets the inner lining. This seam type is also used to hide material edges. To make the seam thinner, the edges are often skived before stitching, and then the fabric may be hammered flat.

## Stock fitting

Stock fitting is an assembly operation that is done away from the main assembly. The separate outsole components are assembled on the stock fitting line before they are taken to the main assembly line. Stock fitting reduces the operations on the main line so the main shoe assembly lines can run faster. Stock fitting allows for quality inspections and more complicated operations that can't be done on the main line.

## String lasted

A shoe upper has a string sewn into the bottom perimeter of the upper. The string is pulled to stretch the upper down onto the last. This can only be used on fabric uppers.

## Strobel sock or Strobel board

The Strobel is the fabric or non-woven material, used to finish the bottom of a shoe upper. The worker uses a Strobel machine to make a Strobel stitch to attach the Strobel board to the upper. It was invented by a guy named Strobel.

## Suede leather or split leather

Suede leather is leather created from the fibrous part of the hide left once the top-grain of the rawhide has been separated from the hide. During the splitting operation, the top grain and drop split are separated. Suede is "fuzzy" on both sides.

## Super tuff

Super Tuff is a very common, non-woven reinforcement material, found in all types of shoes. You will find super tuff behind punched holes and metal hardware.

## Synthetic leather

Man-made material, often a composite made of two layers. A backing layer made of woven or non-woven polyester fibers combined with an external surface by "dry" lamination process or by "wet" liquid processes.

## T/T payment

T/T stands for telegraphic transfer, or wire transfer, a form of bank transfer. T/T payments are a fast and inexpensive way to transfer money overseas. T/T's can be risky for buyers because the money goes into the suppliers' bank account directly, usually before the buyers receive their goods. For companies with a long-running record of trust, the T/T is fast and easy.

## Taped shoe last

A shoe last is covered with two or three layers of masking tape. Once the last is covered, the shoe design can be drawn onto the tape. Once the design is complete, the tape can be removed and laid flat to create the shoe pattern.

## Taped upper or taped shoe upper

A fast way to design a new shoe pattern, or to see your design come to life is to tape over another shoe and draw your new design. In our busy design office, we sometimes box up the taped uppers and send them directly to the factory.

## Throat of the shoe

The throat of the shoe is the opening where the shoe tongue is attached, and that is spanned by the laces. The throat is generally surrounded by the shoes' eyestay.

## Toe box

The toe area of the shoe. Different styles will have different toe box sizes and shapes. Fashion shoes may have tight, pointed tips while work boots have extra space for steel toe inserts.

## Toe puff

Toe puff is the reinforcing material used to hold the shape of the toe box. It can be thermoplastic, which is easily shaped with heat, leather, or fabric. It also comes in many styles from soft to firm.

## Toe spring

The toe spring of a last, shoe, or pattern is simply how much the front tip is off the ground. A stiff hiking boot may have a 15mm toe spring, while a slip-on casual shoe may have a 5mm toe spring. As a general rule, the stiffer the shoe sole, the more toe spring you need for a normal rolling stride.

## Toe tip

The pattern part on the front of the shoe. Usually reinforced.

## Shoe tongue

The shoe tongue pads the top of the foot. It is connected to the top of the vamp at the base of the eyestay. The tongue may have elastic centering straps attached to the edge or a tab that can be held by the laces. Depending on the shoe style, the tongue may be a single layer of leather or an inch of PU foam.

## Top line

The top edge of the shoe's ankle opening or the top edge of the outsole.

## Top-grain leather

Top-grain leather, the most common leather used in high-end leather products, is the second-highest quality. It has the "split" layer separated away, making it thinner and more pliable than full-grain. Its surface has been sanded, and a finish coat added to the surface which results in a colder, plastic feel with less breathability, and it will not develop a natural patina.

## Tread or shoe tread

The part of the shoe that contacts the ground. The shoe tread is most commonly made of rubber.

## Tru-buck Leather

Sueded cow leather that is covered with a thin coating of PU (Polyurethane). The coating is slightly brushed to make a smooth matte finish. The final product is generally a solid color leather looking product. This material is still classified as leather for import duty.

## Try on

Also called "in-store feel," "try on" is the initial feeling when a shoe is tested in-store. A very soft upper and footbed can give a shoe a very good "try-on" but will quickly flatten or compress upon wearing. The footbed and lining can make or break the try on feeling.

## Vamp or shoe vamp

The vamp is the area on top of the toes. The vamp is often made from breathable mesh or has perforations for venting.

## Vulcanize

The process of heating raw rubber to cure it. This process creates crosslinks inside the rubber compound bonding it together. Before the rubber is vulcanized, it is stretchable, gummy, and easy to tear. After being vulcanized, it's tough and ready to wear.

## Vulcanizing Oven

A vulcanizing oven or tank is a steam heated pressure vessel used to cure vulcanized shoes. 500 to 1,000 pairs may be heated at one time. The heating process fuses the outsole rubber parts together and to the upper of the shoe.

## Wedge or midsole wedge

The EVA foam midsole of a shoe, thinner in the front and taller in the heel. When you use the word "wedge", you are usually referring to a die cut midsole part.

## Wholesale price

The wholesale price of an item is what the retail store pays to buy an item from the shoe brand or "wholesaler." The wholesale price is generally 50% of the retail price. A big store may negotiate a price discount of a few percent from the wholesaler.

## Width or shoe width

The width of a shoe is measured in letters such as AAA, AA, A, B, C, D, E, EE, EEE, and EEEE, 4A, 3A, 2A, A, B, C, D, E, 2E, 3E, 4E, 5E, and 6E, or N (narrow), M (medium), R (regular), and W (wide). These letters refer to the width of the shoe as measured at the ball of the foot.

CPSIA information can be obtained
at www.ICGtesting.com
Printed in the USA
LVHW070743211122
733503LV00009B/394